JOHN E. GRAY AND ALBERT GÜNTHER

THE LIZARDS OF
AUSTRALIA AND NEW ZEALAND

With an introduction by Glenn M. Shea

Published in cooperation with the
Australasian Affiliation of Herpetological Societies

SOCIETY FOR THE STUDY OF AMPHIBIANS AND REPTILES · 1995

EDITOR'S NOTE

This reprint comprises two different titles that cover the same subject and utilize the same set of plates. "The Zoology of the Voyage of H.M.S. Erebus & Terror, under the command of Captain Sir James Clark Ross, R.N., F.R.S., during the years 1839 to 1843," edited by John Richardson and John Edward Gray, was issued in at least 24 parts over the years 1844–1875. "Reptiles," as here reprinted and which constitutes the first chapter in volume 2 of the assembled work, was issued in two sections, the first of which, by Gray, includes pages 1–8 and lithographic plates 1–4, 8–9, 12–14, and 20. This section, which was part 6 of the series, was issued in February 1845, according to an original printed wrapper in the editor's collection. The second and concluding section, by Albert Günther, includes pages 9–19 and lithographic plates 5–7, 10–11, and 15–19. This section constituted part 24 of the series and was issued in June 1875, according to an original printed wrapper in the library of the Zoological Society of London. This collation of plates in these two sections differs from that given in the "Catalogue of the Books . . . in the British Museum (Natural History)," volume 4, page 1698, 1913, but is based on a complete copy of the 1845 section in original wrappers. Further publication details are given by Günther on page 9. In some copies of the complete "Reptiles" chapter, the 10 plates originally issued in 1845 have been reprint-ed by a photographic method on glossy paper; perhaps, after the 30-year hiatus in publication, the stock of the original lithographic plates was exhausted and the stones effaced, so that in order to supply complete copies of the chapter on reptiles in 1875, photolithographs were produced to avoid the greater cost of re-drawing them on stone. This reprint, however, has been made from the original lithographic versions of all 20 plates. Regarding Gray's "The Lizards of Australia and New Zealand in the Collection of the British Museum," the date printed on the title page and repeated on a printed label on the front wrapper (1867) is confirmed in *Zoological Record*, volume 4, page 126, 1868. All 18 plates included with this book are original lithographs and are identical to the plates included in the "Voyage," minus plates 5 and 6 as explained by Günther on page 9. Thus, plates 7, 10–11, and 15–19 were issued for the first time in 1867 and plates 5 and 6 only in 1875.

The Society is greatly indebted to Glenn Shea for contributing the introduction to this reprint and to Gerry Swan and Aaron M. Bauer for their editorial assistance. The cooperation of the Australasian Affiliation of Herpetological Societies in producing this volume is gratefully acknowledged. We also thank the following persons for their bibliographic assistance: Ann Datta (Natural History Museum, London) and Ann Sylph (Zoological Society of London).

FACSIMILE REPRINTS IN HERPETOLOGY

KRAIG ADLER, *Editor*   TIMOTHY D. PERRY, *Associate Editor*

Issues in the *Facsimile Reprints in Herpetology* series can be purchased from the Publications Secretary, Robert D. Aldridge, Department of Biology, St. Louis University, 3507 Laclede, St. Louis, Missouri 63103, USA (*telephone*: area code 314, 977–3910 or 977–3916; *fax*: area code 314, 977–3658). A list of all Society publications, including those of The Ohio Herpetological Society and the *Catalogue of American Amphibians and Reptiles*, is printed at the end of this book; additional copies of this list are available from Dr. Aldridge. *Facsimile Reprints* are published irregularly and ordered by separate subscription, although Society members receive a substantial pre-publication discount. Persons having suggestions for future *Facsimile Reprints* should contact the Editor: Kraig Adler, Cornell University, Neurobiology and Behavior, Mudd Hall, Ithaca, New York 14853–2702, USA.

Members of the Society receive a quarterly technical journal (*Journal of Herpetology*) and a quarterly news journal (*Herpetological Review*). Currently, dues are US$25.00 for students, $40.00 for all others, world-wide; institutional subscriptions are $70.00. There is an additional charge of $25.00 for airmail delivery outside the USA. Society members receive substantial discounts on *Herpetological Circulars*, *Facsimile Reprints*, and on books in the *Contributions* series. The *Catalogue* is available by separate subscription at a cost of US$15.00 per annual series of 25 accounts ($3.00 surcharge for airmail delivery). Apply to the Society's Treasurer, Karen L. Toepfer, P.O. Box 626, Hays, Kansas 67601–0626, USA. Overseas customers can make payments in USA funds or by International Money Order. All persons may charge to MasterCard or VISA (include account number and expiration date).

JOHN EDWARD GRAY, ALBERT GÜNTHER, AND THE LIZARDS OF AUSTRALIA AND NEW ZEALAND

GLENN M. SHEA[*]

INTRODUCTION

THE PUBLICATIONS HERE REPRINTED REPRESENT three attempts over the 31-year period from 1845 to 1875 to produce an illustrated account of the lizard fauna of Australia and New Zealand. They are the first monographic publications that deal exclusively with the herpetofaunas of Australia and New Zealand, and the exquisite lithographs which illustrate them are the first published drawings of many members of the herpetofaunas of these two countries. Indeed, some of the illustrations are among the most detailed and lifelike ever produced of Australian and New Zealand reptiles, no mean feat when it is remembered that all were prepared from dead (and in some cases dried and mounted) museum specimens.

In addition, these publications mark the end of the first major period of the discovery of the Australian and New Zealand herpetofaunas and the beginning of the next, and chronicle changes in herpetological knowledge over this period, a time marked by the waning of the career of one of the authors, John Edward Gray, and the flowering of the career of the other, his successor, Albert Günther.

THE SCIENTIFIC EXPLORATION OF AUSTRALIA AND NEW ZEALAND

Scientific study of the Australian herpetofauna began with a collection of reptiles and amphibians sent back to England by John White, surgeon to the First Fleet, and described by George Shaw and John Hunter in 1790 in an appendix to White's account of the voyage (White 1790; Cogger 1993; Shea 1993). During the next 70 years, knowledge of the Australian herpetofauna grew rapidly as a result of several collections sent to

the British Museum, London (now in the Natural History Museum, London) and Muséum National d'Histoire Naturelle, Paris. Collections were made primarily by sea-based expeditions of the Australian coastline, by a few limited overland expeditions, and by individual private collectors who were largely based in and around the few settlements then in Australia, particularly Hobart, Sydney, Swan River, King George Sound, and Port Essington (Cogger 1993).

Among the major sea-based expeditions that collected Australian herpetological material were Baudin's expedition of 1800–1804 (Péron 1807; Baudin 1974; Bonnemains et al. 1988) and de Freycinet's 1817–1820 expedition (de Freycinet 1824–1842), both from France, and the British-funded expeditions led by Philip Parker King between 1818 and 1822 (King 1827) and George Grey in 1837–1839 (Grey 1841), as well as the voyages of H.M.S. *Beagle*, both the celebrated 1832–1836 voyage with Charles Darwin (Darwin 1846; Nicholas and Nicholas 1989) and subsequent surveys in 1837–1843 under the command of John Lort Stokes (Stokes 1846), and the 1846–1850 voyage of H.M.S. *Rattlesnake* (MacGillivray 1852) towards the end of this period. The major overland expeditions were that of Edward John Eyre from Adelaide to King George Sound in 1840–1841 (Eyre 1845), and several from Sydney to the Liverpool Plains and Darling Downs between 1823 and 1828 by the botanist Allan Cunningham (Favenc 1888). Among the private collectors, the two most notable names were John Gilbert, collector for the ornithologist John Gould, in Western Australia and at Port Essington, and the Tasmanian naturalist Ronald Campbell Gunn.

DESCRIPTIONS OF COLLECTIONS

The extensive Australian collections, which were made by the Baudin expedition and subsequent French voyages of exploration and which are held in the museum in Paris, were the source of numerous new species described by herpetologists

*Deptartment of Veterinary Anatomy
 University of Sydney
 Sydney, New South Wales 2006, Australia

and biologists such as Cloquet, Cocteau, Cuvier, Daudin, Lacepède, Lesson, Quoy and Gaimard, Schlegel, and Tschudi. By the 1830s, the collections in Paris were so extensive and representative of then-known herpetological diversity that the herpetologists at the museum, André-Marie-Constant Duméril, his son Auguste-Henri-André Duméril, and Gabriel Bibron began the production of a nine-volume encyclopedic treatment of the known herpetofauna of the world, the "Erpétologie Générale" (1834–1854), in which were included descriptions of many new species and genera.

At the same time as the Dumérils and Bibron were producing their great work, additional collections from Australia and New Zealand were arriving at the British Museum, where they were studied by John Edward Gray (12 February 1800–7 March 1875). In December 1824, as one of his first tasks at the museum, Gray was given the job of compiling a catalogue of the reptile collections, although he was not formally appointed to the museum staff until May 1837. In May 1840, following the death of the incumbent, J. G. Children, Gray became Keeper of the Zoological Collections (Gunther 1975). The successive receipt of collections from King, Gilbert, Grey, and Stokes from Australia, and from Dieffenbach from New Zealand, together with scattered specimens from other sources, resulted in a series of papers (Gray 1825, 1827, 1831a, 1831b, 1831c, 1832, 1835a, 1835b, 1838–1839, 1841a, 1841b, 1842a, 1842b, 1842c, 1842d, 1842e, 1843, 1845a, 1846a, 1846b) describing new species of Australian and New Zealand reptiles and amphibians, generally published either as appendices in the journals of the various expeditions, as abbreviated catalogues and classifications

of reptiles, or as papers in Gray's own journal, the *Zoological Miscellany* (reprinted by the Society for the Study of Amphibians and Reptiles in 1971).

In 1845, at about the time that Gray received a collection of reptiles made by the Antarctic Expedition led by Sir James Clark Ross, the British Museum published the second of his four reptile catalogues, the "Catalogue of the Specimens of Lizards in the Collection of the British Museum." The production of the zoological results of the Antarctic Expedition ("The Zoology of the Voyage of H.M.S. Erebus & Terror") was well in hand at the time of Gray's "Catalogue," which refers to accounts in the "Zoology," even giving plate numbers for three taxa (plate 12, *Tropidolepisma nitida* [=*Egernia kingii*]; plate 13, *T. kingii* [=*E. kingii*]; plate 14, *T. major* [=*E. major*]), and it is clear that Gray envisaged his herpetological account in the "Zoology" as including a summary document of the lizard fauna of Australia and New Zealand, using the relevant accounts from his catalogue, together with a series of lithographs representing most of the known species.

Unfortunately, the production of "The Zoology of the Voyage of H.M.S. Erebus & Terror"

FIGURE 1. John Edward Gray (left) and Albert Günther (right).

temporarily ceased in 1848, at which time only the ichthyological results had been completely published. Mammal, bird, reptile, and insect sections were left incomplete, ending abruptly in mid-text, while the accounts of the crustaceans and molluscs had yet to begin to appear. Only a few of the lithographs were included in these first installments. Gray's account of the lizards of Australia and New Zealand, here reprinted, ended at page 8, and only plates 1–4, 8–9, 12–14, and 20 had appeared. The arrangement of the species and the morphological detail in the accounts is taken almost directly from his catalogue, ending part of the way through his genus *Mocoa* (though plates 12–14 illustrated species in the unpublished section).

The decade following the completion of Gray's series of reptile catalogues and the cessation of the publication of the "Zoology" marked the end of an era in Australian herpetology. Gray became embroiled in arguments with the newly appointed Supervisor of the Zoological Collections, Richard Owen, the flow of new specimens from the Antipodes temporarily waned with the end of the period of British sea-based exploration, and Gray largely ceased writing on Australian reptiles apart from tortoises and crocodiles, although he remained Keeper until his retirement in December 1874 (Gunther 1975). Similarly, the output of papers based on the Paris collection was reduced following the retirement and deaths of the Dumérils and Bibron and the end of French exploration in the Australian region.

The new era of Australian herpetology began in the late 1850s and early 1860s with the appointment of Albert Günther (3 October 1830– 1 February 1914) to the staff of the British Museum, and the beginning of a series of herpetological papers from Wilhelm Peters in Berlin, Gerard Krefft in Sydney, Franz Steindachner in Vienna, and Charles Girard in the United States, the latter two working with the collections made by Austrian and American expeditions, respectively. A new generation of private collectors was at work, including Francis Houssemayne du Boulay in Western Australia, Richard Schomburgk in Adelaide, Edward Dämel and Amalie Dietrich in Queensland, and George Masters in many parts of Australia.

Gray's health deteriorated in the 1860s and in 1867, perhaps frustrated by the lack of further progress with "The Zoology of the Voyage of H.M.S. Erebus & Terror" (his temper had wors-

ened with his loss of health; Gunther 1975), he decided to attempt publication of the collection of lizard lithographs anew. The result was "The Lizards of Australia and New Zealand," chronologically the second of the publications in this facsimile edition (although bound here as the third). With the exception of plates 5 and 6, for which the lithographic plates had been accidentally destroyed by the printer, this monograph included the full set of 20 reptile plates intended for the "Zoology," accompanied by a list of the lizards known from Australia and New Zealand. The latter was still arranged, where possible, in the classification he employed in his "Catalogue of Lizards," but incorporated additional new species, genera, and synonymies made in the intervening 23 years. The majority of these were due to just three publications, one by Peters (1863), based on a collection made in Adelaide by Schomburgk, another by Günther (1867), largely based on collections received from du Boulay and Krefft, and the third by Steindachner (1867), based on the material collected by the *Novara* expedition.

At around the time of Gray's death, funding finally became available to complete "The Zoology of the Voyage of H.M.S. Erebus & Terror." Günther, who replaced Gray as Keeper of Zoology, discovered proofs of the two missing lithographs, and was able to get them redrawn by the original artist, thus completing the set of illustrations. However, rather than simply continue Gray's text as taken from his 1845 "Catalogue," Günther prepared the third of the papers here reprinted, a new list of the lizards of Australia and New Zealand, still faithful to Gray's classification, and incorporating locality data, but without descriptions. He also added newly described species, genera, and synonymies from the literature, and included descriptions of five new species: *Hinulia gastrosticta* (=*Eulamprus quoyii* [Duméril and Bibron]), *Hinulia pallida* (=*Eremiascincus fasciolatus* [Günther]), *Silubosaurus depressus* (=*Egernia depressa*), *Stenodactylopsis tesselatus* (=*Diplodactylus tesselatus*), and *Grammatophora caudicincta* (=*Ctenophorus caudicinctus*).

VOYAGE OF H.M.S. *EREBUS* AND *TERROR*

The voyage of *Erebus* and *Terror*, under which banner two of the three publications here reprinted fall, was an expedition under the command of Sir James Clark Ross sent by the British Admiralty to explore the limits of Antarctica. Leaving England on 19 September 1839, with Dr. R. M'Cormick on board the *Erebus* as medical officer, naturalist, and geologist, the expedition passed south, landing at Madeira in October, the Canary Islands and Cape Verde Islands in November, St. Paul's Rocks and Trinidad in December, St. Helena in February, 1840, Cape Town in March-April, and the Kerguelen Islands between May and July, before arriving at Hobart in Tasmania in mid-August 1840. The expedition stayed in Hobart until mid-November, a period of three months, during which time M'Cormick made several short trips around the Hobart area, and two longer trips, the first overland to Launceston and George Town between 11 and 20 October, passing inland as far as Tunbridge, Lake Sorell, Hamilton, and New Norfolk, and the second by sea to Port Arthur later that month.

On leaving Hobart, the expedition sailed south into Antarctic waters before returning to Hobart on 7 April 1841. After a second three-month stay in Hobart, the expedition departed 6 July 1841 for Sydney, arriving at Garden Island on 14 July. The expedition remained in Sydney until 5 August. Near the end of this period, M'Cormick made a day visit to Parramatta. The expedition then sailed to New Zealand, where it stayed in the Bay of Islands, near Paihia, for the period 17 August to 23 November 1841, before sailing south again for Antarctica. During the period in New Zealand, collecting was concentrated around Paihia, although M'Cormick travelled as far as Waimate and Russell (then Russelton), and up the Kawakawa (then Kava Kava) River.

Following the second Antarctic sojourn, the expedition visited the Falkland Islands between 6 April and 7 September 1842, and Tierra del Fuego between 21 September and 6 November, before returning home via Cape Town (April 1843), St. Helena and Ascencion Island (May), Rio de Janeiro (June) and the Azores (July), arriving in England on 7 September 1843 (M'Cormick 1884).

HERPETOLOGICAL COLLECTIONS

Although the full herpetological results of the expedition did not reach publication, some indication of the limited collections can be gained from the lizard and snake specimens identified in the catalogues of the lizards and snakes in the British Museum (Gray 1845*b*; Günther 1858) as originating from the Antarctic Expedition, or from Lieutenant Alexander Smith, Gray's nephew, who accompanied the expedition (Gray 1845*c*).

Two species and eight specimens of Australian elapid snake were reported by Günther and subsequent authors: *Austrelaps superbus* (as *Hoplocephalus superbus*; three specimens collected by the expedition in "Australia," one by Smith in "Van Diemen's Land," all paralectotypes of the species) and *Drysdalia coronoides* (as *H. coronoides*, two collected by Smith, two presented by the Admiralty from "Van Diemen's Land," paralectotypes of the species). All eight specimens are still in the Natural History Museum, London (Coventry and Rawlinson 1980; Rawlinson 1991).

Gray reported four species of Australian skinks in the collection, mostly without detailed localities, but all species common in Tasmania: two specimens of *Cyclodomorphus casuarinae* (Duméril and Bibron), ten *Egernia whitii* (Lacepède), ten *Pseudemoia entrecasteauxii* (Duméril and Bibron), and three *Tiliqua nigrolutea* (Quoy and Gaimard). These were reported as *Omolepida casuarinae*, *Hinulia whitei*, *Mocoa entrecasteauxii*, and *Cyclodus nigroluteus*, respectively. Of these, two of the *Egernia* were collected by Smith. The specimens of these four species are still present in the collection of the Natural History Museum, London.

The New Zealand material was identified as belonging to two species of skinks and two of geckos. The skinks were identified by Gray as *Mocoa zelandica* Gray (two specimens from the Admiralty) and two series from the Admiralty and Smith which were described as a new species, *M. smithii* (now *Oligosoma smithii*). Problems with the identity of these specimens have been discussed by McCann (1955) and Hardy (1977). The two geckos, represented by a single specimen each, are still known by the names used by Gray: *Naultinus elegans* Gray and *N. grayii* Bell. Although most of the New Zealand collection lack precise locality data, it is likely that all are from the Bay of Islands region.

The only other lizard identified as from the expedition by Gray (1845*b*) is one of two skink specimens on which he based the name *Euprepis* (now *Mabuya*) *stangeri*, ostensibly from South Africa, although the species is only known from the Cape Verde Islands. The specimen is not now identifiable in the British Museum collection (Boulenger 1887).

THE ARTIST

All but possibly one of the exquisite lithographs which form the heart of this reprint are the work of George Henry Ford (1809–1876). Ford was born in South Africa, the son of a farmer. As a child, he was encouraged to draw by the biologist Andrew Smith, who recommended him for employment at the museum in Cape Town, and employed Ford to illustrate his "Illustrations of the Zoology of South Africa." Ford moved to England with Smith on the latter's return in 1837, and was employed by the British Museum. He became a close friend of Günther and drew a number of herpetological lithographs for both Gray and Günther (Gunther 1975). In addition to the lithographs appearing here, he also produced three lithographs of Australian lizards and snakes illustrating Gray's (1846a) appendix to Stokes' journal.

Plate 20 is unique in being labelled "J. Ford." The style is similar to the other plates, and it is not known if this is a different artist or merely a misprint.

LITERATURE CITED

Baudin, N. T. 1974. The journal of Post Captain Nicolas Baudin Commander-in-Chief of the Corvettes *Géographe* and *Naturaliste* assigned by order of the Government to a voyage of discovery (transl. by C. Cornell). Libraries Board of South Australia, Adelaide. xxi, 609 pages.

Bonnemains, J., E. Forsyth, and B. Smith. 1988. Baudin in Australian Waters. The Artwork of the French Voyage of Discovery to the Southern Lands 1800–1804. Oxford University Press, Melbourne. 347 pages.

Boulenger, G. A. 1887. Catalogue of the Lizards in the British Musuem (Natural History). Vol. 3. Lacertidae, Gerrhosauridae, Scincidae, Anelytropidae, Dibamidae, Chamaeleontidae. British Museum, London. 575 pages.

Cogger, H. G. 1993. History of discovery of the Reptilia, p. 92–97. *In* C. J. Glasby, G. J. B. Ross, and P. L. Beesley (eds.), Fauna of Australia. Vol. 2A. Amphibia & Reptilia. Australian Government Publishing Service, Canberra.

Coventry, A. J., and P. A. Rawlinson. 1980. Taxonomic revision of the elapid snake genus *Drysdalia* Worrell 1961. Memoirs of the National Museum of Victoria, 41: 65–78.

Darwin, C. 1846. Journal of researches into the natural history and geology of the countries visited during the voyage of H.M.S. *Beagle* round the world, under the command of Capt. Fitz Roy, R.N. 2 vols. Harper & Brothers, New York.

Eyre, E. J. 1845. Journals of expeditions of discovery into Central Australia and overland from Adelaide to King Georges Sound in the years 1840–1; sent by the colonists of South Australia, with the sanction and support of the Government; including an account of the manners and customs of the aborigines and the state of their relations with the Europeans. 2 vols. T. and W. Boone, London.

Favenc, E. 1888. The history of Australian exploration from 1788 to 1888. Turner & Henderson, Sydney. xv, 474 pages.

Freycinet, L. de. 1824–42. Voyage autour du monde, entrepris par ordre du Roi, sous le ministère et conformément aux instruction de S. Exc. M. le Vicomte du Bouchage, secrétaire d'état au Département de la Marine, exécuté sur les corvettes de S.M. l'*Uranie* et la *Physicienne*, pendant les années 1817, 1818, 1819 et 1820. (7 vols. plus atlas [4 vols.]). Pillet Aîné, Imprimeur-Libraire, de l'Imprimerie Royale, Paris.

Gray, J. E. 1825. A synopsis of the genera of reptiles and Amphibia, with a description of some new species. Annals of Philosophy, ser. 2, 10(3): 193–217.

—. 1827. Reptilia, p. 424–434. *In* P. P. King, Narrative of a survey of the intertropical and western coasts of Australia. Performed between the years 1818 and 1822. Vol. 2. John Murray, London.

—. 1831a. A synopsis of the species of the Class Reptilia, p. 1–110. *In* E. Griffith and E. Pidgeon, The Animal Kingdom arranged in conformity with its organization, by the Baron Cuvier, member of the Institute of France, &c. &c. &c. with additional descriptions of all the species hitherto named, and of many not before noticed. Vol. 9. The Class Reptilia arranged by the Baron Cuvier, with specific descriptions. Whittaker, Treacher, and Co., London.

—. 1831b. Synopsis Reptilium; or short descriptions of the species of Reptiles. Part 1. Cataphracta. Tortoises, Crocodiles, and Enaliosaurians. Treuttel, Würtz & Co., London. viii, 85 pages.

—. 1831c. Description of a new genus of ophisaurean animal, discovered by the late James Hunter. Zoological Miscellany, 1: 14.

—. 1832. [Three new animals brought from New Holland by Mr Cunningham]. Proceedings of the Zoological Society of London, 1832: 39–40.

—. 1835a. Characters of a new genus of reptiles (*Lialis*) from N.S.W. Proceedings of the Zoological Society of London, 1834: 134–135.

—. 1835b. [Mr Gray exhibited a specimen of a toad]. Proceedings of the Zoological Society of London, 1835: 57.

—. 1838–39. Catalogue of the slender-tongued saurians, with descriptions of many new genera and species. Annals and Magazine of Natural History, ser. 1, 1(4): 274–283; 1(5): 388–394; 2(10): 287–293; 2(11): 331–337.

—. 1841a. A catalogue of the species of reptiles and Amphibia hitherto described as inhabiting Australia, with a description of some new species from Western Australia, and some remarks on their geographical distribution, p. 422–449. *In* G. Grey, Journals of two expeditions of discovery in North-west and Western Australia, during the years 1837, 38, and 39, under the authority of Her Majesty's Government. 2 vols. T. and W. Boone, London.

—. 1841b. Description of some new species and four new genera of reptiles from Western Australia, discovered by John Gould, Esq. Annals and Magazine of Natural History, ser. 1, 7(42): 86–91.

—. 1842a. Synopsis of the species of prehensile-tailed snakes, or family Boidae. Zoological Miscellany, 2: 41–46.

—. 1842*b*. Description of some hitherto unrecorded species of Australian reptiles and batrachians. Zoological Miscellany, 2: 51–57.

—. 1842*c*. Description of some new species of reptiles, chiefly from the British Museum collection. Zoological Miscellany, 2: 57–59.

—. 1842*d*. Monographic synopsis of the water snakes, or the family Hydridae. Zoological Miscellany, 2: 59–68.

—. 1842*e*. Description of two hitherto unrecorded species of reptiles from New Zealand; presented to the British Museum by Dr Dieffenbach. Zoological Miscellany, 2: 72.

—. 1843. Descriptions of the reptiles and Amphibia hitherto observed in New Zealand, p. 202–206. *In* E. Dieffenbach, Travels in New Zealand with contributions to the geography, geology, botany, and natural history of that country. Vol. 2. John Murray, London.

—. 1845*a*. Descriptions of some new Australian animals, p. 405–411. *In* E. J. Eyre, Journals of expeditions of discovery into Central Australia and overland from Adelaide to King Georges Sound in the years 1840–1; sent by the colonists of South Australia, with the sanction and support of the government; including an account of the manners and customs of the aborigines and the state of their relations with the Europeans. Vol. 1. T. and W. Boone, London.

—. 1845*b*. Catalogue of the Specimens of Lizards in the Collection of the British Museum. Edward Newman, London. 289 pages.

—. 1845*c*. Reptiles, p. 1–8, plates 1–4, 8–9, 12–14, and 20. *In* J. Richardson and J. E. Gray (eds.) (1844–75), The Zoology of the Voyage of H.M.S. *Erebus & Terror*, under the command of Captain Sir James Clark Ross, R.N., F.R.S., during the years 1839 to 1843. Vol. 2. Longman, Brown, Green, and Longmans, London.

—. 1846*a*. Descriptions of some new Australian reptiles, p. 498–504. *In* J. L. Stokes, Discoveries in Australia; with an account of the coasts and rivers explored and surveyed during the voyage of H.M.S. *Beagle*, in the years 1837–38–39–40–41–42–43. By command of the Lords Commissioners of the Admiralty. Also a narrative of Captain Owen Stanley's visits to the islands in the Arafura Sea. Vol. 1. T. and W. Boone, London.

—. 1846*b*. A new genus of sea-snake from Port Essington. Annals and Magazine of Natural History, ser. 1, 18(119): 284.

Grey, G. 1841. Journals of two expeditions of discovery in North-west and Western Australia, during the years 1837, 38, and 39, under the authority of Her Majesty's Government. 2 vols. T. and W. Boone, London.

Günther, A. 1858. Catalogue of Colubrine Snakes in the Collection of the British Museum. British Museum, London. 281 pages.

—. 1867. Additions to the knowledge of Australian reptiles and fishes. Annals and Magazine of Natural History, ser. 3, 20(115): 45–68.

Gunther, A. E. 1975. A century of zoology at the British Museum through the lives of two keepers 1815–1914. Wm. Dawson & Sons, Ltd., London. 533 pages.

Hardy, G. S. 1977. The New Zealand Scincidae (Reptilia: Lacertilia): a taxonomic and zoogeographic study. New Zealand Journal of Zoology, 4(3): 221–325.

King, P. P. 1827. Narrative of a survey of the intertropical and western coasts of Australia. Performed between the years 1818 and 1822. 2 vols. John Murray, London.

MacGillivray, J. 1852. Narrative of the voyage of H.M.S. *Rattlesnake*, commanded by the late Captain Owen Stanley, R.N., F.R.S. &c. during the years 1846–1850. Including discoveries and surveys in New Guinea, the Louisiade Archipelago, etc. to which is added the account of Mr. E. B. Kennedy's expedition for the exploration of the Cape York Peninsula. 2 vols. T. & W. Boone, London.

McCann, C. 1955. The lizards of New Zealand: Gekkonidae and Scincidae. Dominion Museum Bulletin, 17: viii, 1–127.

M'Cormick, R. 1884. Voyages of discovery in the Arctic and Antarctic seas, and round the World: being personal narratives of attempts to reach the North and South Poles; and of an open-boat expedition up the Wellington Channel in search of Sir John Franklin and Her Majesty's ships "Erebus" and "Terror," in Her Majesty's boat "Forlorn Hope," under the command of the author. To which are added an autobiography, appendix, portraits, maps, and numerous illustrations. 2 vols. Sampson Low, Marston, Searle, and Rivington, London.

Nicholas, F. W. and J. M. Nicholas. 1989. Charles Darwin in Australia. Cambridge University Press, Cambridge. 175 pages.

Péron, F. 1807. Voyage de découvertes aux Terres Australes, exécuté par ordre de Sa Majesté l'Empereur et Roi, sur les Corvettes le *Géographe*, le *Naturaliste*, et la Goelette le *Casuarina*, pendant les années 1800, 1801, 1802, 1803 et 1804. Vol. I. Imprimerie Impériale, Paris. 496 pages.

Peters, W. 1863. Übersicht der von Hrn. Richard Schomburgk an das zoologische Museum eingesandten Amphibien, aus Buchsfelde bei Adelaide in Südaustralien. Monatsberichte der Königlichen Akademie der Wissenschaften zu Berlin, 1863: 228–236.

Rawlinson, P. A. 1991. Taxonomy and distribution of the Australian tiger snakes (*Notechis*) and copperheads (*Austrelaps*) (Serpentes, Elapidae). Proceedings of the Royal Society of Victoria, 103(2): 125–135.

Shea, G. M. 1993. The anatomist John Hunter (1728–1793), the Eastern Bluetongue Skink *Tiliqua scincoides* (Squamata: Scincidae) and the discovery of herbivory in skinks. Archives of Natural History, 20(3): 303–306.

Steindachner, F. 1867. Reptilien, p. 1–98, plates I–III. *In* B. von Wüllerstorf-Urbair (ed.). Reise der Österreichischen Fregatte *Novara* um die Erde in den Jahren 1857, 1858, 1859. Zoologischer Thiel. Erster Band (Wirbelthiere). Kaiserlich-Königlichen Hof- und Staatsdrucke, Wien.

Stokes, J. L. 1846. Discoveries in Australia; with an account of the coasts and rivers explored and surveyed during the voyage of H.M.S. *Beagle*, in the years 1837–38–39–40–41–42–43. By command of the Lords Commissioners of the Admiralty. Also a narrative of Captain Owen Stanley's visits to the islands in the Arafura Sea. 2 vols. T. and W. Boone, London.

White, J. 1790. Journal of a Voyage to New South Wales with sixty-five plates of non descript animals, birds, lizards, serpents, curious cones of trees and other natural productions. J. Debrett, London. 299 pages.

REPTILES.

I. — THE REPTILES OF AUSTRALIA.

Dr. Shaw, in the Appendix to White's 'Journal of a Voyage to New South Wales,' in 1790, first described and figured some of the Reptiles observed by White in New Holland. Some of the specimens he brought home having been placed in the collection of the British Museum, were more systematically described by the same naturalist in his 'General Zoology,' and his work on the Animals of New Holland.

Lacepède, in the 'Annales du Muséum,' (iv. 18), described several Reptiles from the same country, and redescribed several of those which had been already noticed by Shaw and White.

Capt. Flinders, in his 'Voyage to Terra Australis,' 1814, mentions the occurrence of two kinds of Turtles (*Chelonia*) one on the north coast of New Holland (ii. 154), and the other on the east coast (ii. 382).

Peron and Lesueur, during their voyage with Captain Baudin on the coasts of Australia, collected many specimens of this class of animals, which were deposited in the Museum of the Garden of Plants, and a few of which were noticed by Oppel in preparing the Reptile part of Cuvier's 'Règne Animal.' Others have been described by Messrs. Duméril and Bibron, in their 'Erpetologie Générale,' now in the course of publication. Some others were described by me during my visit to Paris, when I was preparing the Synopsis of Reptiles, which appeared in Griffith's translation of Cuvier's 'Animal Kingdom,' which must only be considered as an abstract of the notes prepared for my 'Synopsis Reptilium.'

In the Appendix to Capt. Philip Parker King's 'Voyages in Australia,' I described some new species discovered by that navigator, especially the very curious Frilled Lizard, which is figured in that work. From time to time, as specimens from that country have been kindly presented to the Museum by different collectors, as my late friend Allan Cunningham, Mrs. Joseph Wright, and others, I have described the specimens in the 'Proceedings of the Zoological Society,' and other scientific periodical publications.

In the Appendix to His Excellency Capt. George Grey's Australia, I attempted to bring together these scattered materials, and formed a list of the different species which had been described as coming from Australia, adding to it descriptions and figures of the new Australian species, chiefly sent home by Governor Grey and Mr. Gilbert, from the west coast, then in our collection; and since that time 1 have, in my 'Zoological Miscellany,' described several additional species, which have, in the mean time, been sent to England from the north coast of Australia by Mr. Gilbert, who is employed by Mr. Gould to collect specimens for him in different parts of that continent.

In the Zoology of the Voyages of the French ships, l' Uranie, la Coquille and l' Astrolabe, some Australian Reptiles have been figured and described by MM. Quoy and Gaimard and M. Lesson; but unfortunately, though the descriptions of the specimens are long and apparently full, yet they are so general, and the figures of the species, though good for artistic effect, are so destitute of scientific detail, that it is often impossible to determine which of the Australian species they are intended to represent; and the specimens from whence they were described, do not appear to be in the collection of the French Museum, for MM. Duméril and Bibron do not refer to them in their work.

In the Appendix to Dr. Dieffenbach's New Zealand, I described the Reptiles he had brought from those islands; Mr. Bell, in the 'Zoology of the Beagle,' has described and figured another species from the same country, which was brought home by my friend, Mr. Darwin: and another species has since been discovered by my nephew, Lieut. Alexander Smith, R.N., who accompanied the Antarctic Expedition.

Order I. Lizards, (Sauria).

Mouth not dilatable. Jaws toothed. The lower jaw-bones being united by a bony suture in front. Eye with distinct eyelids. Drum of the ears generally distinct, exposed. Nostrils lateral, nasal cavities separated by a long cavity. Limbs 4, distinct, rarely in such a rudimentary state as to be hidden under the skin. Toes generally distinct, clawed, for walking or climbing. Body elongate, rounded, covered with imbricate granular scales. Ribs distinct, mobile, and with a distinct sternum. Tail elongate, tapering, rarely prehensile, generally covered with whorls of scales. Egg with a hard skin. Young not undergoing any metamorphosis.

The Gryphi, containing the *Ichthyosauri*, *Plesiosauri*, the recently discovered *Rhyncosauri*, and other Lizard-like fossils of the lias and new red sandstone, which have nearly the same formation of the skull, the pendant ear-bones &c. of the Saurias, are easily distinguished from them by their doubly cupped vertebræ and usually paddle-like feet, like Cetacea amongst Mammalia.

Sect. I. Squamata.

Body covered with overlapping or granular scales. Nostrils lateral. The skull formed of separate bones. The nasal cavities separated by a bony septum. The ear-bone external, pendent, and only articulated to the skull. Tongue free, elongate, nicked at the tip, often entire. The lungs free in the cavity of the thorax. The vent a linear cross slit. The male organ and vagina forked. Vertebræ with a convex surface fitting into a concave surface in the preceding joint. Oviparous, rarely viviparous. The eggs when deposited covered with a more or less coriaceous shell.

Sub-order I. Leptoglossæ.

Tribe I. Cyclosaura.

Scales of the belly square (very rarely rhombic, keeled), in cross bands, of the back and tail rhombic, imbricate, or circular and subgranular, placed in cross rings, of the sides generally granular, rarely like the back. Tongue elongate, flattened, base sometimes sheathed, generally free, only attached to the gullet by a long frenum, with two elongate cylindrical horny tips. Tail elongate, with whorls of scales, generally conical, tapering, sometimes compressed, with two elevated crests above.

Family. Monitoridæ.

Head with minute polygonal shields. Teeth adnate to the inner side of the jaws. Tongue elongate, slender, retractile into a sheath at its base. Scales small, roundish, placed in cross rings, those of the sides like those of the neck. Legs 4, strong. Toes 5-5, compressed, subequal. Thighs poreless. Superorbital plate bony. Old World, near water.

The species of this family are confined exclusively to the Eastern World and Australasia. Of the twenty-two species described in the Catalogue of the Lizards in the British Museum, the last complete work on the species of Reptiles that has appeared, six are peculiar to Australia, eleven are found in India, Borneo and New Guinea, and five in Africa.

1. *Tail round without any keel above.* Terrestræ.

Odatria, *Gray.*

Nostrils ovate, longitudinal, subanterior. Teeth compressed, acute. Tail elongate, round, not keeled above. Scales large, sharply keeled, subspinose. Back with elongate, narrow, keeled scales. Ventral shield elongate. Toes rather unequal, elongate.

This genus is easily known from the terrestrial Monitors of Africa, by the larger size and keeled form of the caudal scales.

Besides the Australian species, there is one, *O. Timorensis*, from the Island of Timor, first described by me in Griffith's Animal Kingdom, ix. 36.

The Dotted Odatria. Odatria punctata.

Plate 1.

Odatria punctata, *Gray, Ann. N. H.* ii. 394. *Grey's Trav. Austr.* ii. 422. *Cat Rept. B. M.* 7.
Monitor tristis, *Schlegel, Abbild.* 73.

Grey olive, with narrow, black, reticulated lines, bearing large hexagonal spots; head, limbs and tail blackish, with a few pale spots, dark-banded; ventral shield twice as long as broad; tail round; scales over the eye small, granular; male? with a tuft of conical spine-like scales on each side of the vent.

The young is blackish, with cross rings of white spots; head closely white speckled; limbs white dotted. Very young grey, with numerous narrow dark cross bands.

Inhabits West Australia and Port Essington.

The Eyed Odatria. Odatria ocellata.

Plate 2.

Odatria ocellata, *Gray, Cat. Rept. B. M.* 8.

Black, with rather large yellow rings; limbs and tail yellow-spotted; tail round; scales of the tail broad, oval, spinose; scales over the eyes small, granular; ventral shields twice as long as broad.

Inhabits N.W. coast of Australia. Benjamin Bynoe, Esq., R.N.

Like *O. punctata*, but the scales of the back, and the spinose scales of the tail are much larger. The scales of the back are bluntly keeled, of the tail square, nearly as broad as long, sharply and strongly keeled, spinose; in *O. punctata* they are nearly twice as long as broad, and only subspinose.

2. *Tail triangular, compressed, and with a doubly toothed crest above. Nostril small, round.*

Monitor, *Gray.*

Polydædalus, *Wagler.* Uaranus, *Fitz.*

Nostrils small, round, in the middle between the apex of the muzzle and the front angle of the eye. Tail elongate, compressed, with a double-edged keel above. Toes elongate, unequal, strong. Teeth rounded.

GOULD'S MONITOR. Monitor Gouldii.

Plate 3.

Monitor Gouldii, *Schlegel. Gray, Cat. Rept. B. M.* 12.
Hydrosaurus Gouldii, *Gray, Ann. N. H.* i. 394. *Grey's Trav. Austr.* ii. 422.

With 2 yellow streaks on the side of the neck; scales over the eyes small, granular, of forehead larger; ventral shields small, longer than broad.

Inhab. Western and North-western coast of Australia.

HYDROSAURUS, *Wagler.*

Tupinambis, part, *Fitz.*

Nostrils oblong, longitudinal, near the apex of the muzzle. Tail elongated, with a double-edged keel above. Toes unequal, elongate. Teeth compressed, sharp-edged, denticulated.

This genus is divided into two sections; some have the scales over the orbit small and equal, others have a series of larger ones in the middle of the small ones. All the Australian species belong to the former division. The second section contains two species; one, *M. bivittatus*, found in India, Borneo and the Philippines, the other, *M. prasinus*, at New Guinea.

* *Scales over the orbit equal. Neck with lunate bands.*

The LACE LIZARD. Hydrosaurus varius.

Lacerta varia, *Shaw, White's Journ. N. S. W.* 246, t. 3, *f.* 2. *Nat. Misc.* iii. *t.* 83.
Uaranus varius, *Merrem, Tent.* 58. *Dum. et Bib. E. G.* iii. 491. *Gray, King's Voy.* ii. 427.
Tupinambis variegatus, *Daud. Rept.* iii. 76. *Kuhl, Beytr.* 125.
Hydrosaurus varius, *Wagler, Syst.* 164. *Gray, Ann. N. H.* i. 394. *Cat. Rept. B. M.* 12.

Grey, with black cross bands, which are lunated over the nape; scales of the orbit very small, equal.

Inhab. New Holland.

BELL'S LACE LIZARD. Hydrosaurus Bellii.

Uaranus Bellii, *Dum. et Bib. E. G.* iii. 493, *t.* 35, *f.* 1. *Gray, in Grey's Trav. Austr.* ii. 422.
Hydrosaurus Bellii, *Gray, Cat. Rept. B. M.* 13.

Pale, body and tail with broad black cross bands; scales of the orbits dilated, equal.

Inhab. Australia ??

This species is only known from a specimen in Mr. Bell's collection, and one in the Paris Museum.

** *Scales of the orbit equal, small. Neck spotted like back.*

The GIGANTIC LACE LIZARD. Hydrosaurus giganteus.

Plate 4.

Hydrosaurus giganteus, *Gray, Cat. Rept. B. M.* 13.

Brown, back and tail with cross bands of large black-edged white spots; neck and under side of body pale, with large black round reticulations; legs white-spotted; toes

rather short, strong; shields of the head subequal, convex, over the orbits very small, granular.

Inhab. N. coast of New Holland.

The largest species of the genus. The specimen in the British Museum is 78 inches long. It was discovered and described by Capt. Stokes, R.N.

Tribe II. GEISSOSAURA.

Scales of the belly and (almost always) of the back and sides, rounded, quincuncial, imbricate, formed of a more or less thick, vascular, bony plate, covered with a thin epidermis, often showing the vessels through it. Sides rounded, covered with scales like those of the back. Tongue narrow, short, flat, slightly nicked at the end. Head covered with regular many-sided shields (rather scale-like in (*Lialisidæ*). Neck not contracted. Body fusiform or subcylindrical. Femoral pores none, (except in *Pygopus* and *Lialis*).

A. *Eyes distinct, exposed. Eyelid rudimentary. Head conical.*

Fam. GYMNOPHTHALMIDÆ.

Nostrils lateral, in a single nasal plate, without any supranasal above it. Teeth conical, simple. Palate toothless. Tongue scaly, nicked at the tip. Eyes naked. Eyelids rudimentary, circular, ring-like, and immoveable. Ears distinct. Body fusiform. Limbs 4, weak, unequal. Femoral pores none.

CRYPTOBLEPHARUS, *Cocteau, Weigmann.*

Ablepharus, part, *Dum. et Bib.*

Head pyramidical. Frontoparietal plate single. Nostrils lateral, in a single nasal, supranasal none. Eyelid rudimentary, circular. Ears moderate, open, denticulated in front. Tongue flat, scaly, nicked at the tip. Palate toothless. Body fusiform. Scales smooth, or very finely and indistinctly grooved. Legs 4. Toes 5-5, unequal, rather compressed. Tail roundish, tapering, acute. Preanal scales in three rows.

* *Eyelid complete, with a series of larger scales above.*

The PETE. Cryptoblepharus Boutonii.

Scincus plagiocephalus, *Peron, Mus. Paris.*
S. Boutonii, *Desjard. Ann. Sci. Nat.* xxii. 298.
S. arenarius, and S. furcatus, *Schlegel, Mus. Leyd.*
S. aureus, *Mus. Paris.*
Cryptoblepharis Peronii, *Coct. Scincoides*, i. *t.* *Mag. Zool. t.* *Dum. et Bib. E. G.* v. 813.
C. Leschenaultii, *Coct. Scin*, i. *t.*
C. Boutonii, *Gray, Cat. Rept. B. M.* 64.
Ablepharus pœcilopleurus, *Weigm. N. Act. N. Cur.* xv. 183, *t.* 8, *f.* 1. *Gray, Ann. N. H.* ii. 335. *Grey's Trav. Austr.* ii. 426. *Seba, Thes.* ii. *t.* 2, *f.* 9-10.
Tiliqua Buchanani, *Gray, Ann. N. H.* ii. 291.

Olive or bronzed, brown-varied. Scales black-streaked. Eyelid circular, scaly, with the three upper scales largest. Ears moderate, suboval, open, simple-edged. Rostral plate very large, triangular. Preanal plates 6 or 7, nearly equal.

Inhab. Western Australia, the Isle of France, Timor.

** Eyelid incomplete, no scales between the eye and eyebrow above.

The EYED PETE. Cryptoblepharus lineo-ocellatus.

Plate 5, fig. 1.

Ablepharus lineo-ocellatus, *Dum. et Bib.* v. *E. G.* 817.
Cryptoblepharus lineo-ocellatus, *Gray, in Grey's Trav. Austr.* ii. 427. *Cat. Rept. B. M.* 65.

Back grey or reddish, with 4 series of white-edged black spots, and edged with a pale streak, and a black-edged white streak on each side. Upper lip white. Eyelid circular, covered with small equal scales, without any between the eye and superciliary plates. Rostral plate small, very broad, 6-sided. Frontal plate broader than long. Ears moderate, suboval, with 2 or 3 denticulations in front. Head short.

Inhab. Swan River, W. Australia.

MORETHIA, *Gray.*

Head pyramidical. Frontoparietal shields rough. Nostril lateral, in a small shield with a small supranasal above it, and a smaller nasoloreal shield behind it. Eyelid rudimentary, circular. Ears moderate, open, denticulated in front. Body fusiform. Scales smooth. Legs 4, weak. Toes 5-5, unequal, rather compressed. Tail roundish, tapering, acute. Preanal scales rather larger.

This only differs from *Cryptoblepharus* in the nasal shields. It is as if the nasal shield of that genus was divided into three small plates.

The MORETHIA. Morethia anomalus.

Plate 5, fig. 2.

Morpethia anomalus, *Gray, Cat. Rept. B. M.* 65.

Olive bronzed, black-spotted; eyelid scales equal; ears with 3 or 4 small denticulations in front.

The young have a dark-edged white streak on the sides.

Inhab. Western Australia.

MENETIA, *Gray.*

Head subquadrate. Muzzle rounded. Rostral plate moderate. Nostril lateral, in an oblong nasal shield; supranasal none; frontoparietal shield single, rhombic. Eyes moderate; pupil round. Eyelid rudimentary, circular. Ears small, covered with the scales. Body elongate, fusiform, subcylindrical, rounded on the sides. Scales smooth. Legs 4, weak. Toes 4-5, slender, rather compressed, unequal, clawed. Tail cylindrical, tapering.

The MENETIA. Menetia Greyii.

Plate 5, fig. 3.

Menetia Greyii, *Gray, Cat. Rept. B. M.* 66.

Olive bronzed, with a narrow streak externally edged with a very narrow black line.

Inhab. West Australia.

I have dedicated this genus to Capt. George Grey, the Governor of South Australia, who has exerted himself to make us acquainted with the animals of the Australian continent.

MICULIA, *Gray.*

Head conical. Muzzle rounded. Rostral plate rather larger, with a straight edge behind. Nostrils lateral in the middle of 2 transverse nasal scales, edging the back of the rostral; supranasal none; frontoparietal shield double. Eyes moderate; pupil round. Eyelids rudimentary, circular, granular. Ears none visible. Body subcylindrical, rounded on the sides. Scales smooth. Legs 4, weak. Toes 4-4, slender, rather compressed, simple, unequal, clawed, the two middle front subequal, longest, the third hinder very long. Tail cylindrical, tapering.

The MICULIA. Miculia elegans.

Plate 5, fig. 4.

Miculia elegans, *Gray, Cat. Rept. B. M.* 66.

Olive, with a dark streak on each side, with a narrow white edge below; beneath pale whitish; tail brown-dotted; eyelid interrupted above.

Inhab. Western Australia, Mr. Gilbert.

b. *Head wedge-shaped.*   *Rostral rather produced.*

LERISTA, *Bell.*

Muzzle rather wedge-shaped. Rostral plate large, bent back on the upper and lower part of the muzzle. Nostril lateral, in a large nasal plate; supranasal none. Eyelid rudimentary, circular, granular. Ears distinct, very small. Palate with a slight triangular nick behind. Scales smooth. Tail conical. Legs 4. Toes 2-3, unequal, clawed, subcylindrical, simple. Preanal plates 2. "The ear-hole is so small that it was overlooked by Mr. Bell."

The LERISTA. Lerista lineata.

Lerista lineata, *Bell, Pr. Z. Soc.* 1833, 99. *Zool. Journ.* v. 393, *t.* 26, *f.* 2. *Gray, Ann. N. H.* ii. 335. *Cat. Rept. B. M.* 66. *Dum. et Bib. E. G.* v. 825.

Greenish grey, with 2 black streaks.

Inhab. New Holland.

Only known from a single specimen in the collection of Mr. Bell.

Fam. PYGOPIDÆ.

Head pyramidical, shielded, short, with 2 or 3 pair of narrow frontal shields, similar to and behind the nasal shield, with 2 large vertebral shields. Nostrils oblong, in a ring-like shield, in the lower angle of the band-like transverse nasal, appearing in the suture between the outer angle of the nasal, the front loreal shield and the lower labial plates. Throat covered with small scales. Teeth conical simple. Palate toothless, with a broad longitudinal groove. Tongue flat, scaly in front, velvety behind, rounded and nicked at the end. Ears distinct, exposed; tympanum sunk. Eyelid rudimentary, circular, immoveable, scaly. Body cylindrical, elongate. Ventral shields broad behind, in 2 or 4 series. Tail with 3 series of broader shields, the central broadest. Limbs 2, posterior, rudimentary, undivided, scaly, on the sides of the vent.

PYGOPUS, *Fitz.*, *Merrem.*

Bipes, *Cuv.*   Hysteropus, *Dum. et Bib.* (!)

Head short, truncated. rounded.   Rostral plate large, with 2 parietal and a pair of occipital plates.   Pupil circular.   Scales of the back keeled.   Ear ovate.   Vent with a series of pores in front.   Hinder limbs elongate, ovate, compressed, scaly.   Tail cylindrical, rather tapering.

The PYGOPUS.   Pygopus lepidopodus.

Pypogus lepidopus, *Gray, Cat. Rept. B. M.* 67.
Bipes lepidopodus, *Lacep. Ann. Mus. H. N.* iv. 193, 209, *t.* 55, *f.* 1. *Schinz, Abbild, t.* 42, *f.* 2.
Pygopus lepidopus, *Merrem, Tent.* 77.
Hysteropus lep. *Bory, Res. Erpet.* 142, *t.* 27, *f.* 2.
H. Novæ Hollandiæ, *Dum. et Bib. E. G.* v. 828, *t.* 55.
Sheltopusik Novæ Hollandiæ, *Oppel, Rept.* 40.

Coppery grey, with 5 series of oblong, 4-sided, white-edged, black spots and some oblique black streaks on the side of the neck; muzzle with 2 pair of broad transverse frontals, similar in shape to the nasals.

Inhabits Australia.

The SCALY-FACED PYGOPUS.   Pygopus squamiceps.

Plate 8, fig. 3.   Animal and head.

Pygopus squamiceps, *Gray, Cat. Rept. B. M.* 68.

Muzzle with 5 series of frontal plates; grey, with a series of small spots on each side.

Inhab. W. Australia.

I have only seen a single specimen; it may only prove a monstrosity of the former, with which it agrees in most characters, except those above mentioned.

DELMA, *Gray.*

Pygodactylus, part, *Weigm.*

Head elongate, shielded, with 2 parietal and a pair of large occipital shields.   Rostral plate transverse, moderate.   Eye circular; pupil elliptical, erect.   Ears ovate, open, simple-edged.   Body subcylindrical.   Tail tapering.   Scales smooth.   Hinder limbs short, scaly.   Vent without any pores in front.

FRASER'S DELMA.   Delma Fraseri.

Delma Fraseri, *Gray, Zool. Misc.* 14. *Grey's Trav. Aus.* ii. 427, *t.* 4, *f.* 3. *Cat. Rept. B. M.* 68.

Olive, head white, with 4 more or less confluent black bands; sides of neck white-spotted, beneath white.

Inhab. New Holland.

Fam. APRASIADÆ.

Nostrils small, in the suture between the top of the front upper labial and the anterior frontal.   Head small, half conic, shielded.   Muzzle rather produced, acute.   Frontals large, 2 pair, covering the cheeks.   Vertebral shield large, elongated, 6-sided.   Superciliary shields 2 pair, small.   Labials few, large.   Eyelid rudimentary, circular, edged with a series of small scales.   Pupil round.   Ears hidden under the scales.   Body and tail cylindrical, tapering, covered with hexagonal scales and rather broader ventral shields.   Limbs none.

APRASIA, *Gray.*

Limbs none.   Scales smooth.

By some mistake, the slip containing the description of this genus in my Synopsis of Slender-tongued Saurians, (*Ann. N. H.* ii. 362), accidentally got into the wrong place, with *Tiliqua,* instead of being near *Anguis.*

The APRASIA.   Aprasia pulchella, *Gray, Ann. N. H.* ii. 332. *Grey's Trav. Austr.* ii. 428—438, *t.* 4, *f.* 2. *Cat. Rept. B. M.* 68.

Pale brown, with a series of brown spots, one spot in the centre of each scale; sides with the spots more connected, forming interrupted streaks; lips yellow.

Inhab. Western Australia.

Fam. LIALISIDÆ.

Head covered with rather imbricate scales.   Cheeks scaly.   Muzzle flattened in front.   Nostrils in the hinder edge of a small nasal shield, in front of the face-ridge.   Eyelid rudimentary, circular, scaly.   Pupil elliptical, erect.   Ears distinct.   Body elongate, subcylindrical.   Scales oval, smooth, imbricate.   Belly with 2, tail with 1, series of larger shields.   Limbs 2, posterior, short, undivided, flat, scaly.   Tail rather tapering, elongate.   Vent with a series of pores in front, each placed in the front edge of a scale.

LIALIS, *Gray.*

The only genus.

BURTON'S LIALIS.   Lialis Burtoni, *Gray, Proc. Z. Soc.* 1834, 134.   *Grey's Trav. Austr.* ii. 437, *t.* 3, *f.* 1.   *Zool. Misc.* 52. *Cat. Rept. B. M.* 69.   *Dum. et Bib. E. G.* v. 831.

Above grey olive, in spirits, with 5 rather interrupted brown longitudinal streaks, the central streak divided into two over the nape, and united together again over the nose; the outer lateral streaks narrowest and more interrupted, edged with the two colours; beneath blackish grey, with large white spots; lips and streak under ear and along the side of the neck white.

Inhab. Western Australia and Houtman's Abrolhos.

The TWO-LINED LIALIS.   Lialis bicatenata.

Plate 7, fig. 1.

Lialis bicatenata, *Gray, Zool. Misc.* 52. *Cat. Rept. B. M.* 69.

Above brown grey, in spirits, with a series of distant black spots (one on the centre of each scale) along each side of the back; top of the head and nape with an indistinct double band, forming an elongated loop; beneath blackish grey, whitish dotted; chin and throat blackish, white-spotted; lip-shields brown.

Inhab. Western Australia?   May be only a variety of *L. Burtoni,* but very differently coloured.

The DOTTED LIALIS.   Lialis punctulata.

Plate 8, fig. 1.

Lialis punctulata, *Gray, Zool. Misc.* 62. *Cat. Rept. B. M.* 69.

Brownish grey, very minutely black-dotted, beneath darker brownish grey, the two colours separated by a very narrow brown edge and a distinct white line; side of the head and neck dark chocolate brown, edged above with a very narrow, and beneath by a broader white band; front upper and side lower labial plates white, the rest dark brown.

Inhab. North Coast of New Holland, Port Essington.

The body is much thicker and shorter than in either of the other species; the tail is reproduced, so that it is not possible to refer to its comparative length.

I have seen, but cannot procure to examine, what appeared to be a fourth species of this genus, from Australia, with a larger head.

B. *Eyes distinct, eyelids distinct, valvular. Head conical.*

Fam. SCINCIDÆ.

Head subquadrangular, regularly shielded. Rostral plate moderate, erect, sometimes rather produced and transversely keeled. Nostrils lateral in a more or less large nasal shield, with sometimes a supranasal over it, between the nasal and internasal. Body fusiform and subcylindrical. Tail cylindrical or tapering. Scales smooth, keeled, or striated. Limbs 4, more or less strong, sometimes wanting, or rather hidden under the skin. Femoral pores none.

1. *Scales thin, smooth, not striated nor keeled, unarmed. Nasal flat, smooth, without any lunate groove behind the nostril. Tail round, tapering, unarmed.*

B. *Toes compressed, simple. Head subquadrangular. Rostral erect, triangular. Nostril in the middle of the nasal shield. Lygosomina.*

a. *Supranasal plate none. Body fusiform. Lower eyelid covered with scales. Frontoparietal separate.*

HINULIA, *Gray.*

Lygosoma, part, *Dum. et Bib.* Le Keneux, part, *Cocteau.*

Frontal plate oblong. Rostral erect, triangular. Palate toothless, with a deep triangular notch in front. Body fusiform. Scales smooth, thin; the 2 central preanal scales larger than the rest. Tail tapering, roundish. Legs moderate. Toes 5-5, slender, compressed. Heel of the hind feet surrounded with granules.

* *Ears simple in front, roundish.*

GERRARD'S HINULIA.   Hinulia Gerrardii.
Plate 9.

Hinulia Gerrardii, *Gray, Cat. Rept. B. M.* 75.

Silvery grey (when dry), with a broad irregular brown band across the back of the neck, with a streak to the occiput, and a broader one to each fore leg; body with 6, tail with 12 or 14 broad crescent-like cross brown bands, which are spotted with grey when they cross the side; limbs with brownish streaks; head brown above, head-shields black-edged, with a brown streak on the temple, towards the ear; chin white, brown-lined, belly brown-spotted; ear open, simple in front, partly covered by the temple-scales; supraocular plates 3-3, nasal nearly contiguous, frontoparietal contiguous.   Length 14 inches.

Inhab. Australia.

The ELEGANT HINULIA.   Hinulia elegans.
Plate 10, fig. 1.

Hinulia elegans, *Gray, Cat. Rept. B. M.* 75.

Pale brown, back varied with black spots, more close, forming an irregular broad dark streak on the upper part of each side, beneath whitish; chin varied with black; lips and limbs blackish varied; nasal and frontonasal nearly contiguous; ears ovate, open, simple-edged.

Inhab. New Holland.

The SWAN RIVER HINULIA.   Hinulia Greyii.
Plate 10, fig. 2.

Hinulia Greyii, *Gray, Cat. Rept. B. M.* 75.

Olive, black-varied, with a dark-edged yellow streak on each side of the back; sides black-spotted, with a yellow streak below; legs brown-streaked; lip-shields black-edged; ears oblong, smooth-edged; frontal triangular, elongate, frontonasal contiguous, frontoparietal and parietal small, similar; body thick, fusiform.

Inhab. Swan River.

Named in honour of Capt. George Grey, the Governor of South Australia, who discovered the species.

The SLENDER HINULIA.   Hinulia tenuis.
Plate 10, fig. 3.

Tiliqua tenuis, *Gray, Griffith, A. K.* ii. 71. *Ann. N. H.* ii. 291.
Scincus erucatus, *Peron, Mus. Paris.*
Lygosoma erucata, *Dum. et Bib. E. G.* v. 726.
Keneux de Busseuil, *Coct. Tab.*
Hinulia tenuis, *Gray, Cat. Rept. B. M.* 76.

Pale brown, varied, with an irregular-edged brown streak on each side; scales in 8 series; feet long, toes very slender; muzzle rather short; supraocular shields 4; ears round, open, simple-edged; nostrils lateral, nasal triangular, frontonasal nearly contiguous; tail elongate, rather compressed.

Var. with sides white-speckled.

Inhab. W. Australia, Swan River.

The BRONZED HINULIA.   Hinulia inornata.
Plate 10, fig. 4.

Hinulia inornata, *Gray, Cat. Rept. B. M.* 76.

Pale nearly uniform brown bronze above, back with a rather narrow bright yellow rather darker-edged streak on each side; the sides pale, with an indistinct yellow streak on the lower part of each, both streaks extending along the side of the tail; chin and beneath whitish, with rather darker edges to the sides; ears oblong, with 4 or 5 small compressed yellow scales in front.

Inhab. Swan River.

The LINEATED HINULIA.   Hinulia tæniolata.

Hinulia tæniolata, *Gray, Cat. Rept. B. M.* 78.
Lacerta tæniolata, *Shaw, White's Jour. N. H. t.* 32, *f.* 1.
Gray, Griffith, A. K. ix. 68. *Ann. N. H.* ii. 289. *Dum. et Bib. E. G.* v. 734.
Scincus undecim-striatus, *Kuhl, Beytr.* 129.
S. octolineatus, *Daud. Rept.* iv. 285.
S. multilineatus, *Lesson, Voy. Coq. t.* 3, *f.* 2.
Keneux de Lesueur, *Coct. Tab.*

Brown or black, with 6 white streaks, continued and margining the shields of the head; sides brown, with 2 white streaks; tail pale, with 3 tapering streaks; nasals contiguous; scales of the back in 4 series; ears denticulated in front; frontonasal plates contiguous.

Inhab. Australia.

In the British Museum there is the specimen first described by Dr. Shaw, which was brought by Capt. White.

WHITE'S HINULIA.   Hinulia Whitei.

Plate 11, fig. 1.

Hinulia Whitei, *Gray, Cat. Rept. B. M.* 79.
Scincus Whitei, *Lacep. Ann. Mus.* iv. 192.
S. ocellatus, and S. Lewisiensis, *Peron, Mus. Paris.*
S. tæniolatus quadrilineatus, *Merrem, Tent.* 72.
S. moniliger, *Valenc. Mus. Par.*
Lygosoma moniligera, *Dum. et Bib. E. G.* v. 736.
Keneux de White, *Coct. Tab.*
Tiliqua leucopsis, *Gray, Ann. N. H.* ii. 291.

Pale olive, back with a central pale streak, and a regular white-spotted black streak on each side; sides white-spotted; eyelid and ear-lobes white; lips black-varied; scales of the back as long as broad, in 8 series; nasal plates contiguous; ears strongly denticulated in front; frontonasal plates contiguous.

Inhab. Houtman's Abrolhos.

Var. 1. Dorsal streaks each with 2 rows of linear white specks.

Inhab. Swan River.

A stuffed specimen has a central reddish streak on the back.

The NEW ZEALAND HINULIA.   Hinulia ornata.

Plate 11, fig. 2.

Hinulia ornata, *Gray, Cat. Rept. B. M.* 77.
Tiliqua ornata, *Gray, Dieff. N. Z.* ii. 202.

Bright pale brown, varied with black and white spots; sides with an irregular narrow pale streak above; scales with short black streaks, some black on each side, white in the centre; ears moderate, roundish, simple-edged.

Brown, with black and white spots.

Brown, with 3 blackish streaks, sides blackish, edged above and below with an irregular edged pale line.

Inhab. N. Zealand.

** *Ears denticulated in front.*

† *Scales moderate, in 4 series.*

LABILLARDIERE'S HINULIA.   Hinulia Labillardieri.

Plate 11, fig. 3.

Hinulia Labillardieri, *Gray, Cat. Rept. B. M.* 77.
Keneux de Labillardiere, *Coct. Tab.*
Tiliqua Labillardieri, *Gray, Ann. N. H.* ii. 289. *Dum. et Bib. E. G.* v. 734.

Bronze green, speckled or lined with black; sides black, white-dotted, and with 2 white streaks; nasals rhombic, large, nearly contiguous, frontonasal plates separate; ears ovate, slightly denticulated in front; scales of the back large, in 4 series.

Young, in spirits. Bronze green, with a series of round white spots in the black on the sides of the back.

Inhab. W. Australia.

The AUSTRALIAN HINULIA.   Hinulia australis.

Plate 11, fig. 4.

Hinulia australis, *Gray, Cat. Rept. B. M.* 78.
Tiliqua australis, *Gray, Ann. N. H.* ii. 291.
Lygosoma Lesueurii, *Dum. et Bib. E. G.* v. 733. *Gray, Grey's Trav. Austr.* ii. 425.

Pale brown, with a central white-edged brown streak; sides black, with a narrow white streak above, a series of oblong white spots, as if formed of an interrupted streak, and a rather wide indistinct pale streak below; ears half-ovate, with 4 strong teeth in front; temple white, brown-spotted; scales of the back in 4 series.

Var. 1. Back pale, with a white-edged central streak. Back with several white-edged streaks.

Inhab. Houtman's Abrolhos.   Mr. Gould's collection.

Var. 2. Back brown, without a streak.

Inhab. W. Australia and Port Essington.

GILBERT'S HINULIA.   Hinulia Essingtonii.

Plate 7, fig. 2.

Hinulia Essingtonii, *Gray, Cat. Rept. B. M.* 78.
Tiliqua Essingtonii, *Gray, Zool. Misc.* 51.

Pale brown, nape with 3 indistinct black streaks, with a very distinct narrow broadly black-edged silvery streak from the back angle of the eye to over the base of the tail, and with a broader more indistinct streak from the front to the hinder legs; sides of throat brown, white-spotted; chin, under side of limbs and beneath, yellow; tail elongate, brown, with 2 narrow black streaks on each side; limbs brown, with 3 indistinct black-dotted lines; ears large, with 3 small scales on the front edge.

Inhab. Port Essington, North coast of Australia.

Like the preceding, but it has no white-edged central streak, and the lateral streak has indications of a white border to its upper edge.

b. Supranasal plate none. Body fusiform. Lower eyelid with a transparent disk.

MOCOA, *Gray.*

Lygosoma, part, *Dum. et Bib.*

Head subquadrangular. Rostral erect, triangular, convex. Nasal lateral, nearly contiguous, supranasal none, frontoparietal separate or united into one. Palate toothless, nicked behind. Ears oblong, slightly denticulated in front; tympanum deep. Lower eyelid with a central transparent disk. Chin with several pairs of large shields. Body fusiform. Scales smooth, with 3 or 4 black streaks. Limbs 4, strong. Toes 5-5, compressed, unequal. Tail round, tapering, unarmed. Central preanal scales rather larger than the others.

* *Fronto-parietal plate single, lozenge-shaped.*

† *Scales of the back moderate, in 6 series.*

GUICHENOT'S MOCO.   Mocoa Guichenoti.

Plate 7, fig. 3.

Mocoa Guichenoti, *Cat. Rept. B. M.* 80.
Lygosoma Guichenoti, *Dum. et Bib. E. G.* v. 713. *Gray, Grey's Trav. Austr.* ii. 425.

Bronze green, with a blackish streak on each side; scales of the neck moderate; frontoparietal plate single, larger, elongate, lozenge-shaped, frontal triangular, equal-sided; nasal plate small, quite lateral, internasal broad, truncated in front; ear large, nearly circular, open, simple-edged in front; two of the four scales of the last preanal series larger than the rest.

Inhab. King George's Sound.

There is, in the British Museum, a specimen of this species which was sent from Paris by M. Bibron, under the name of *Scincus Duperreyii*, the name which he has applied to the next species in his work. The same kind of error is observable in the other specimen sent at the same time. I should not have observed this mistake, if it did not explain some of the errors into which he has accused me of falling, such as considering his *Scincus Vosmaeri* the same as my *Hagria*, (see *Erp. Gen.* v. 762); my genus and species being absolutely described from his specimen so named, lent to me for the purpose by M. Bibron!

The NEW HOLLAND MOCO.   Mocoa trilineata.

Plate 7, fig. 4.

Mocoa trilineata, *Gray, Cat. Rept. B. M.* 81.
Tiliqua trilineata, *Gray, Ann. N. H.* ii. 291.
Lygosoma Duperreyii, *Dum. et Bib. E. G.* v. 715.

Olive, black-spotted, with a pale streak on each side, sides blackish, white-dotted; ears moderate, oval, front edge covered with 2 scales; nasal lateral, nearly contiguous, frontoparietal plate single, lozenge-shaped, frontal rhombic, short and blunt before, long and acute behind.

Var. 1. Olive, scales of the back and sides black-edged, not spotted.

Var. 2. Olive, black and white spotted, sides blackish, white-dotted.

Inhab. S. Australia.

†† *Scales of the back small, in 8 or 10 series.*

The BLACK-CHINNED MOCO.   Mocoa melanopogon.

Plate 7, fig. 5.

Mocoa melanopogon, *Gray, Cat. Rept. B. M.* 80.

Olive, varied with black, and with 2 or 3 white streaks in some of the scales; side of the head and neck black, with a white streak under the eyes from the back edge of the ear; chin and throat black, with a central white spot on each scale, beneath silvery; nasal lateral, frontonasal contiguous; scales of the back rather small, in 8 or 10 series, of the sides smaller; disk of lower eyelid very large.

Inhab. Port Essington.

††† *Scales of the back very small, in numerous series.*

The EYED MOCO.   Mocoa ocellata.

Plate 7, fig. 1.

Mocoa ocellata, *Gray, Cat. Rept. B. M.* 81.

Olive, varied with numerous sometimes confluent black dots, forming rings on the sides, beneath whitish; scales very small, in many series; nasal rhombic, lateral; disk of lower eyelid large.

Inhab. Australia.

** *Interparietal plates 2, separate.*

† *Ear ovate, partly covered with the scales above.*

ENTRECASTEAUX'S MOCO.   Mocoa Entrecasteauxii.

Plate 7, fig. 2.

Mocoa Entrecasteauxii, *Gray, Cat. B. M.* 82.
Lygosoma Entrecasteauxii, *Dum. et Bib. E. G.* v. 717.

Olive, back with a broad blackish central streak, sometimes with series of spots on the side, sides blackish, with 2 narrow white streaks; nasal plates small, nearly contiguous; temple covered with large scales; transparent disk of the lower eyelid very large; ears moderately open, nearly equal; frontoparietal plate double, frontonasal nearly contiguous.

Inhab. Australia.

The MOKO MOKO.   Mocoa Zelandica.

Plate 7, fig. 3.

Mocoa Zelandica, *Gray, Cat. Rept. B. M.* 82.
Tiliqua Zelandica, *Gray, Dieff. N. Z.* ii. 202.
Tiliqua Moko, *Gray, MSS. Dum. et Bib. E. G.* v. 718.

Pale brown, bronzed, with 2 narrow black-edged bright streaks on each side, the lower one continued down the front of the legs; sides blackish; the frontonasal nearly contiguous, frontoparietal separate, similar to the parietal, nasal nearly contiguous; ears moderate, nearly circular, simple-edged; preanal scales nearly equal, larger; palpebral disk moderate.

Inhab. Cook's Straits, New Zealand, Bay of Islands.

A List of the Saurians *of Australia and New Zealand.* By ALBERT GÜNTHER, M.A., M.D., PHD., F.R.S., V.P.Z.S., *Keeper of the Zoological Department of the British Museum.*

IN the year 1845, when the publication of the Zoology of the " Erebus and Terror" was discontinued, Dr. Gray had already prepared some of the materials for the second part of the account of the Reptiles, and the plates intended for it had been drawn on stone and the majority of them printed. These plates remained unpublished until the year 1867, when, considering it a pity that work so beautifully executed and so useful to the Herpetologist should be lost, he determined to render them accessible by publishing them as a collection of figures of Australian Lizards. Thus, then, appeared a fasciculus under the title " The Lizards of Australia and New Zealand in the collection of the British Museum," consisting of a nominal list and eighteen plates. Of these plates, plates 7, 10, 11, and 15 to 19 had not been previously published; the others had already appeared in the Zoology of the " Erebus and Terror," with the exception of plates 5 and 6, of which proofs only had been printed, the drawings having been afterwards inadvertently effaced by the lithographic printer. Having fortunately discovered the proofs of these two plates, with the figures named in Dr. Gray's handwriting, in a collection of miscellaneous drawings given to me by him, I induced the publisher of the present edition to have them re-lithographed by Mr. Ford (the same artist who had drawn the originals), as the figures had been referred to by Dr. Gray in the preceeding pages as well as in the "Catalogue of Lizards." Thus I believe, all the figures of Reptiles executed for the "Zoology of the Erebus and Terror," are now before the public.

After the lapse of nearly thirty years, there were serious difficulties in the way of simply continuing the letterpress as originally planned and abruptly terminated on p. 8, and it was finally determined to give a complete list of all the species of Australian and New Zealand Saurians at present known, with references to the principal works and figures and indications of their habitats. Descriptions of a few new species lately received by the British Museum have been added.

CROCODILIA.

1. CROCODILUS POROSUS.

Crocodilus porosus, (Schneid.), Günth. Rept. Brit. Ind. p. 62.
Queensland.

2. CROCODILUS JOHNSTONI.

Crocodilus johnstoni, Krefft, Proc. Zool. Soc. 1873, p. 334; Gray, *ibid,* 1874, p. 177, pl. 27.
Cardwell, Rockingham Bay.

RHYNCHOCEPHALIA.

3. HATTERIA PUNCTATA. Plate 20.

Hatteria punctata, Gray, Zool. Misc. p. 72 ; Günth, Phil. Trans. 1867, pp. 595—629; pls. 26—28.
New Zealand (North Island).

LACERTILIA.

VARANIDÆ.

4. ODATRIA PUNCTATA. Plate 1.

Odatria punctata, Gray, Catal. Liz. p. 7.
Northern and Western Australia. (Port Essington. Perth).

5. ODATRIA SEMIREME.

Odatria semireme, Peters, Berl. Monatsber. 1869. p. 65.
Port Essington, Cape York.

6. ODATRIA OCELLATA. Plate 2.

Odatria ocellata, Gray, Catal. Liz. p. 8.
Northern and Western Australia. (Nicol Bay).

C

7. Monitor gouldii. Plate 3.

Monitor gouldii, Gray, Catal. Liz. p. 12.
Queensland ; Northern and Western Australia, (Port Essington, Shark's Bay) ; Adelaide.

8. Monitor chlorostigma.

Monitor chlorostigma, Schleg. Abbild. neu. Amphib. pl. 22, fig. 6 (head).
Celebes, Ceram, Borneo, Solomon Island, Cape York.

9. Hydrosaurus varius.

Hydrosaurus varius, Gray, Catal. Liz. p. 12.
Australia.

10. Hydrosaurus bellii.

Hydrosaurus bellii, Dum. & Bibr. Erp. Géner. III, p. 493, pl. 35, fig. 1 ; Gray, in Grey, Trav. Austr. II, p. 422.
North-eastern Australia.

11. Hydrosaurus giganteus. Plate 4.

Hydrosaurus giganteus, Gray, Catal. Liz. p. 13.
Northern and Southern Australia.

Gymnopthalmidæ.

12. Cryptoblepharus pœcilopleurus. Plate 5, fig. 2.*

Cryptoblepharus pœcilopleurus, Wiegm. Nov. Act. Acad. C. Leop. XV. 1835, p. 202, tab. 18, fig. 1 ; Günth. Proc. Zool. Soc. 1874, p. 296.
South Sea Islands ; Northern, Western and Southern Australia. (Adelaide, Swan River).

13. Cryptoblepharus lineo-ocellatus.

Cryptoblepharus lineo-ocellatus, Gray, in Grey's Trav. Austr. II, p. 427.
Swan River ; Kangaroo Island.

14. Morethia anomala. Plate 5, fig. 1.

Morethia anomala, Gray, Catal. Liz. p. 65.
Eastern, Western and Southern Australia. (Adelaide, Sandhurst, Rockhampton).
This lizard differs in nothing from *Cryptoblepharus lineo-ocellatus,* except in having the supranasal separated by a suture from the nasal ; and it appears to me very doubtful whether the presence or absence of a supranasal can be always used as a generic character.

15. Menetia greyii. Plate 5, fig. 4.

Menetia greyii, Gray, Catal. Liz. p. 66.
Western and Southern Australia, (Adelaide).

16. Miculia elegans. Plate 5, fig. 3.

Miculia elegans, Gray, Catal. Liz. pl. 66.
Western Australia.

17. Lerista lineata.

Lerista lineata, Bell, Zool. Journ. V. p. 323, tab. 26, fig. 2 ; Dum. & Bibr. Erp. gén. V. p. 825.
Eastern and Western Australia. (Swan River).

Pygopodidæ.

18. Pygopus lepidopus. Plate 8, fig. 3.

Pygopus lepidopus, (Lacép.), Günth. Ann. & Mag. Nat. Hist. 1867, XX, p. 45.=*Hysteropus novæ hollandiæ,* Dum. & Bibr. V. p. 828, pl. 55.=*Pygopus squamiceps,* Gray, Cat. Liz. p. 68.
Western, Southern and Eastern Australia. Rare in Tasmania.

19. Pygopus gracilis.

Pygopus gracilis, (Mus. Lugd.)=*Pletholax gracilis,* Cope, Proc. Ac. N. Sc. Philad. 1874, p. 229.
South-western Australia.

20. Delma fraseri.

Delma fraseri, Gray, in Grey's Trav. in Austral. II, p. 427, tab. 4, fig. 3 ; Günth. Ann. Mag. Nat. Hist. 1873, p. 145.=*Delma grayi,* Smith, Ill. Zool. S. Afr. Rept. pl. 76, fig. 2.=*Delma mölleri,* Lütken, Nat. Foren. Vid. Medd. 1862.
Western and Southern Australia, (Perth, Champion Bay, Nicol Bay, Adelaide).

Aprasiidæ.

21. Aprasia pulchella.

Aprasia pulchella, Gray, in Grey's Trav. in Austral. II, p. 438, tab. 4, fig. 2 ; Günth. Ann. Mag. Nat. Hist. 1873, Aug. p. 145.=*Aprasia octolineata,* Peters, MB. Berl. Acad. 1863, p. 233.
Western and Southern Australia, (Swan River, Adelaide).

---

* In the original proof of this plate the names attached by Dr. Gray to two of the figures, are evidently confused ; he appears to have intended fig. 2 for *Cr. lineo-ocellatus,* but it is without any doubt taken from a specimen of *Cr. pœcilopleurus* which at the time of the preparation of the plate was already in his hands.

LIALIDÆ.

22. LIALIS BURTONI. Plate 8, fig. 2.

Lialis burtonii, Gray in Grey's Journ. in Austral. II, p. 437, tab. 3, fig. 1, tab. 5, fig. 4.
Western Australia, (Houtman's Abrolhos, Champion Bay, Swan River).

22A. LIALIS LEPTORHYNCHA.

Lialis leytorhyncha, Peters, MB. Berlin Acad. 1873, p. 605.
Port Mackay.

23. LIALIS PUNCTULATA. Plate 8, fig. 1.

Lialis punctulata, Gray, Zool. Misc. p. 52, & Cat. Liz. p. 69 ; Günth. Ann. & Mag. Nat. Hist. 1867, XX, p. 46 ; Dum. Cat. Rept. 1851, p. 195.=*Lialis bicatenata*, Gray, Zool. Misc. p. 52, & Cat. Liz. p. 69.
Eastern, Northern and Western Australia, (Sydney, Cape York, Port Essington).

SCINCIDÆ.

24. HINULIA GERRARDI. Plate 9.

Hinulia gerrardi, Gray, Cat. Liz. p. 75,=*Hemisphæriodon gerrardi*, Peters, MB. Berl. Acad. 1867, p. 23.
Queensland, (Rockhampton, Clarence River).

25. HINULIA TENUIS. Plate 10, fig. 1 & Plate 11, fig. 3.

Hinulia tenuis, Gray in Griff. Ann. Kingd. IX, p. 71, & Cat. Liz. p. 76 ;=*Lygosoma erucata*, Dum. Bibr. Erp. Gén. V. p. 726 ;=*Hinulia elegans*, Gray, Cat. Liz. p. 76.
(Plate 10, fig. 1, *H. elegans*; and plate 11, fig. 3, *H. tenuis*).
Eastern and Western Australia, (Sydney, Clarence River, Nicol Bay).

26. HINULIA GASTROSTICTA, Günth.

Allied to *H. elegans*, but with much smaller scales which form from 38 to 41 longitudinal series round the body, there being 82 scales in a series between the chin and vent. The anterior and posterior frontals and the vertical meet in a point. Ear-opening very wide, ovate, without lobed margin. Tail compressed. A narrow whitish band runs from the supraciliary along each side of the back, disappearing about the middle of the trunk. Upper parts greenish-olive, with scattered black specks of the size of a scale irregularly arranged. Sides of the trunk black, with white specks; sides of the tail black-spotted. Lower parts whitish, with more or less numerous black spots longitudinally arranged.

Four specimens from Kangaroo Island, 11 inches long.

Distance of snout from vent	93 mm.
„ „ „ „ ear	20 „
Length of fore leg	28 „
„ third and fourth fingers	8 „
„ hind leg	43 „
„ third toe	9 „
„ fourth toe	15 „
„ fifth toe	8 „

27. HINULIA LABILLARDIERI. Plate 10, fig. 3, (*H. greyii*).

Hinulia labillardieri (Coct.),= *Tiliqua labillardieri*, Gray, Ann. Nat. Hist. II, p. 289,=*Lygosoma labillardieri*, Dum. Bibr. Erp. gen. V. p. 731,=*Hinulia labillardieri*, Gray, Cat. Liz. p. 77,=*Hinulia greyii*, Gray, l. c. p. 76.
Eastern and Western Australia, (King George's Sound, Swan River).

28. HINULIA BRANCHIALIS.

Hinulia branchialis, Günth. Ann. & Mag. Nat. Hist. 1867, XX, p. 47.
Western Australia, (Champion Bay).

29. HINULIA FASCIOLATA.

Hinulia fasciolata, Günth, Ann. & Mag. Nat. Hist. 1867, XX, p. 47.
Queensland, (Rockhampton, Port Curtis).

30. HINULIA STRIATULA.

Hinulia striatula, Steindachner, Novara, Rept. p. 49, (*Euprepes striatulus*).
New South Wales and Western Australia, (Sunday Island).

31. HINULIA ORNATA. Plate 11, fig. 1.

Hinulia ornata, Gray, in Dieffenb. N. Z. II, p. 201, (*Tiliqua*) ; and Cat. Liz. p. 77.
New Zealand.

32. HINULIA SCHOMBURGKI.

Hinulia schomburgki, Peters, MB. Berl. Acad. 1873, p. 231, (*Lygosoma*).
South Australia, (Adelaide).

33. HINULIA AUSTRALIS.

Hinulia australis, Gray, Ann. Nat. Hist. II, p. 291, (*Tiliqua*), and Cat. Liz. p. 77,=*Lygosoma lesueurii*, Dum. Bibr. Erp. gen. V. p. 733.
Western and Southern Australia, (Port Essington, Houtman's Abrolhos, Adelaide).

34. Hinulia essingtoni.

Hinulia essingtonii, Gray, Cat. Liz. p. 78.
North Australia, (Port Essington).

35. Hinulia inornata.   Plate 10, fig. 2.

Hinulia inornata, Gray, Cat. Liz. p. 78.
Northern and Western Australia, (Cape York, Swan River).

This species is not always so plainly coloured as the typical specimen; but generally it is ornamented with black, white edged bands, similar in arrangement to those of *H. australis*. It may be considered a variety of this latter species, but with somewhat smaller and more numerous scales which form 30, and in one specimen even 34 longitudinal series round the body, whilst in the true *H. australis* they are arranged in 26 series only.

36. Hinulia tæniolata.

Hinulia tæniolata, (Shaw); White. Journ. pl. 32, fig. 1; Gray, Cat. Liz. p. 78,=*Lygosoma tæniolatum*, Dum. Bibr. Erp. gen. V. p. 734,=*Scincus multilineatus*, Less. Voy. Coq. pl. 3, fig. 2.
New South Wales.

37. Hinulia whitii.

Hinulia whitii, (Lac.), Gray, Cat. Liz. p. 79,=*Lygosoma moniligerum*, Dum. Bibr. Erp. gen. V. p. 736.
Australia generally, Tasmania, (Kangaroo Island, Houtman's Abrolhos, Swan River, Adelaide, Sydney, Gayndah, Rockhampton).

38. Hinulia pantherina.

Hinula pantherina, Peters, MB. Berl. Acad. 1866, p. 89.
Swan River.

39. Hinulia richardsonii.   Plate 11, fig. 2.

Hinulia richardsonii, Gray, Cat. Liz. p. 79.
Western Australia, (Houtman's Abrolhos, Champion Bay).

40. Hinulia pallida. Günth.

The præfrontal is in contact with the rostral as well as vertical which is much elongate; the anterior and central occipitals similar in shape and size. Seven upper labials. Thirty-two longitudinal series of scales round the middle of the body. Eighty scales in a longitudinal series between the chin and vent. Ear-opening rather small, without projecting scales in front. Limbs well developed. Upper parts light brownish-olive, very indistinctly marbled with darker. Lower parts white.

Distance of snout from vent	71	mm
„ „ „ ear	14	„
Length of fore limb	19	„
„ third and fourth fore toes	5	„
„ hind limb	27	„
„ third hind toe	6	„
„ fourth „	9	„
„ fifth „	4½	„

One specimen from Nicol Bay, is in the British Museum.

41. Mocoa guichenoti.

Mocoa guichenoti, Dum. Bibr. Erp. gen. V. p. 713 (*Lygosoma*),=*Lygosoma duperreyi*, Dum. Bibr. l. c. p. 715, =*Mocoa guichenoti*, Gray, Cat. Liz. p. 80,=*Mocoa trilineata*, Gray, l. cl p. 81.
Southern and Western Australia and Tasmania, (Sydney, Loyalty Island, Swan River).

42. Mocoa microtis.   Plate 7, fig. 2.

Mocoa microtis, Gray, Cat. Liz. p. 83.
Swan River.

43. Mocoa owenii.

Mocoa owenii, Gray, Cat. Liz. p. 272.
Hab. ?

44. Mocoa crassicauda.

Mocoa crassicauda, Hombr. & Jacq. Voy. Austrol. Rept. pl. 4, fig. 1 (*Lygosoma*); Dum. Cat. Méth. p. 172.
New Holland.

45. Mocoa mustelina.

Mocoa mustelina, O'Shaughnessy, Ann. & Mag. Nat. Hist. XIII. 1874, p. 299.
Sydney.

46. Mocoa ocellata.   Plate 7, fig. 3.

Mocoa ocellata, Gray, Cat. Liz. p. 82.
Tasmania.

47. Mocoa entrecasteauxii.   Plate 7, fig. 5.

Mocoa entrecasteauxii, Dum. Bibr. Erp. gen. V. p. 717, (*Lygosoma*); Gray, Cat. Liz. p. 82.
Tasmania.

48. Mocoa metallica.

Mocoa metallica, O'Shaughnessy, Ann. & Mag. Nat. Hist. XIII. 1874, p. 299.
Tasmania.

49. MOCOA MICROLEPIDOTA.

Mocoa microlepidota, O'Shaughnessy, Ann. & Mag. Nat. Hist. XIII, 1874, p. 299.
Tasmania.

50. MOCOA PRETIOSA.

Mocoa pretiosa, O'Shaughnessy, Ann. & Mag. Nat. Hist. XIII, 1874, p. 298.
Tasmania.

51. MOCOA PSEUDOTROPIS.

Mocoa pseudocarinata, O'Shaughnessy, Ann. & Mag. Nat. Hist. XIII, 1874, p. 300.
The name given by Mr. O'Shaughnessy being a "*vox hybrida*," I have changed it for a better term.
Tasmania.

52. MOCOA ZEALANDICA. Plate 7, fig. 4.

Mocoa zealandica, Gray, in Dieffenb. N. Z. II, p. 202, (*Tiliqua*), and Cat. Liz. p. 82,=*Lygosoma moco*, Dum. Bibr. Erp. gen. V, p. 718,=*Mocoa smithii*, Gray, Cat. Liz. p. 82,=*Lygosoma lineo-ocellata*, Dum. Cat. méth. p. 169,=*Mocoa variegata*, Buller, Trans. N. Z. Inst. III, p. 6, pl. 2, fig. 2, see Hutton, ibid. IV, p. 168,=*Mocoa striata*, Buller, l. c.
New Zealand.

53. MOCOA (?) LAXA.

Mocoa (?) *laxa*, Hutton, Trans. N. Z. Inst. IV, 1872, p. 169.
New Zealand.

54. MOCOA GRANDIS.

Mocoa grandis, Gray, Cat. Liz. p. 272.
New Zealand, (South Island).

54b. LYGOSOMELLA ÆSTUOSA.

Lygosomella œstuosa, Girard, in Wilkes Explor. Exped. XX, p. 251, pl. 28, figs. 1—8.
New Zealand.

55. MOCOA NIGROPLANTARIS.

Mocoa nigroplantaris, Peters, MB. Berl. Acad. 1873, p. 744.
New Zealand.

55b. HOMBRONIA UNDOSA.

Hombronia undosa, Girard in Wilkes Expl. Exp. XX, p. 240, pl. 27, figs. 17—24.
New Zealand.

55c. HOMBRONIA FASCIOLARIS.

Hombronia fasciolaris, Girard in Wilkes Expl. Exp. XX, p. 243, pl. 27, figs. 25—32.
New Zealand.

56. CARLIA MELANOPOGON. Plate 7, fig. 7.

Carlia melanopogon, Gray, Cat. Liz. pp. 81 & 272.
North Australia, (Port Essington).

56b. CYCLODINA ÆNEA.

Cyclodina œnea, Girard in Wilkes N. Z. Expl. Exp. XX, p. 236, pl. 26, figs. 9—16.
New Zealand.

57. LYGOSOMA AUSTRALE. Plate 6, fig. 3.

Lygosoma australe, Gray, Ann. Nat. Hist. p. 332, & Cat. Liz. p. 85,=*Hinulia gracilipes*, Steindachner, S. B. Wien. Acad. 1870, LXII, p. 342, tab. 5.
Swan River, Rockhampton, Cape York and Adelaide.

58. LYGOSOMA BOUGAINVILLII.

Lygosoma bougainvillii, Dum. Bibr. Erp. gen. V. p. 716,=*Lygosoma laterale*, Günth. Ann. & Mag. Nat. Hist. 1867, XX, p. 46.
South Australia, (Adelaide, Kangaroo Island).

59. LYGOSOMA PUNCTULATUM.

Lygosoma punctulatum, Peters, MB. Berl. Acad. 1871, p. 646.
North Australia, (Port Bowen, Cape York).

60. LYGOSOMA SCUTIROSTRUM.

Lygosoma scutirostrum, Peters, MB. Berl. Acad. 1873, p. 743.
Port Bowen.

61. COPHOSCINCUS OBSCURUS.

Cophoscincus obscurus, O'Shaughnessy, Ann. & Mag Nat. Hist. XIV, 1874, p. 35.
Queensland.

62. TETRADACTYLUS DECRESIENSIS. Plate 6. fig. 4.

Tetradactylus decresiensis, (Péron), Gray, Cat. Liz. p. 86.
Western Australia, (Swan River, Champion Bay, Kangaroo Island). New South Wales, (King George's Sound).

63. HEMIERGIS DECRESIENSIS. Plate 6, fig. 5.

Hemiergis decresiensis, (Péron), Gray, Cat Liz. p. 86.
Swan River and Adelaide.

64. HEMIERGIS POLYLEPIS.

Hemiergis polylepis, Günth. Ann. & Mag. Nat. Hist. 1867, p. 48.
South Australia, (Kangaroo Island).

65. CHELOMELES QUADRILINEATUS. Plate 6, fig. 2.

Chelomeles quadrilineatus, Dum. Bibr. Erp. gen. V, p. 774.
Western Australia, (Houtman's Abrolhos, Champion Bay, Swan River).

66. CHELOMELES RETICULATUS.

Chelomeles reticulatus, Günth. Ann. & Mag. Nat. Hist. 1873, p. 146.
Clarence River.

67. OMOLEPIDA CASUARINÆ.

Omolepida casuarinæ, Dum. Bibr. Erp. gen. V, p. 749.
Tasmania and South-eastern Australia, (Sydney).

68. LISSOLEPIS LUCTUOSA.

Lissolepis luctuosa, Peters, MB. Berl. Acad. 1866, p. 90, & 1872, p. 776.
South-western Australia.

69. SIAPHOS ÆQUALIS. Plate 6, fig. 1.

Siaphos æqualis, Gray, Cat. Liz. p. 89.
South-eastern Australia, (Sydney).

70. ANOMALPUS VERREAUXII.

Anomalopus verreauxii, Dum. Cat. méth. p. 185; Peters, MB. Berl. Acad. 1867, p. 24; Günth. Ann. & Mag. Nat. Hist. 1867, p. 47=*Siaphos simplex*, Cope, Proc. Phil. Acad. 1864, p. 229=*Anomalopus godeffroyi*, Peters, l. c.
New South Wales and Queensland, (Brisbane, Clarence River).

71. RHODONA PUNCTATA.

Rhodona punctata, Gray, Cat. Liz. p. 89 = *Ronia catenulata*, Gray, in Grey's Trav. Austr. II, p. 437, tab. 4, fig. 1=*Brachystopus lineo-punctulatus*, (Smith MS.) Dum. Cat. méth. p. 186.
Western Australia, (Swan River).

72. RHODONA GERRARDI.

Rhodona gerrardi, Günth. Ann. & Mag. Nat. Hist. 1867, XX. p. 46.
Western Australia, (Swan River, Champion Bay).

73. RHODONA PUNCTATO-VITTATA.

Rhodona punctato-vittata, Günth. Ann. & Mag. Nat. Hist. 1867, XX, p. 46.
Queensland.

74. OPHIOSCINCUS AUSTRALIS.

Ophioscincus australis, Peters, MB. Berl. Acad. 1873, p. 747.
Port Bowen.

75. SORIDIA LINEATA.

Soridia lineata, Gray, in Grey's Trav. Austr. II, p. 428, tab. 3, fig. 2, & Cat. Liz. p. 92 ;=*Pholeophilus capensis*, Smith, Ill. Zool. S. Afr. App. p. 15; Günth. Ann. & Mag. Nat. Hist. 1873, p. 147.
Western Australia.

76. SORIDIA MIOPUS.

Soridia miopus, Günth. Ann. & Mag. Nat. Hist. 1867, XX, p. 370.
Champion Bay.

77. EUMECES ALBOFASCIOLATUS.

Eumeces albofasciolatus, Günth, Ann. & Mag. Nat. Hist. 1872, XX, p. 49.

78. MABOUIA HIEROGLYPHICA.

Mabouia hieroglyphica, Hombr. & Jacq. Voy. Pôle Sud. Rept. pl. 5, fig. 1, (*Lygosoma*) ; Dum. Cat. méth. p. 166.
Tasmania.

79. MABOUIA MACRURA.

Mabouia macrura, Günth. Ann. & Mag. Nat. Hist. 1867, p. 48.
Cape York.

80. BRACHYMELES LEUCKARTII.

Brachymeles leuckartii, Weinland, Abhandl. Senckenb. Ges. IV, 1862, p. 140, tab. 5, fig. 3.
New Holland.

80A. NORBEA (?) ISOLATA.

Norbea (?) isolata, Hutton, Trans. N. Z. Inst. IV, 1872, p. 170.
Bay of Plenty.

81. TRACHYDOSAURUS RUGOSUS.

Trachydosaurus rugosus, Gray in King's Voy. Austr. II, p. 424, & Cat. Liz. p. 102.
Western and Southern Australia, (Houtman's Abrolhos, Sydney).

82. HYDROSAURUS ASPER.

Trachydosaurus asper, Gray, Cat. Liz. p. 103.
Adelaide.

83. CYCLODUS GIGAS.

Cyclodus gigas, (Bodd.), Gray, Cat. Liz. p. 103;=*Cyclodus boddærtii*, Dum. Bibr. Erp. gen. V, p. 752.
Australia generally and Tasmania. (Port Essington, Sydney, Adelaide, Gayndah).

84. CYCLODUS NIGRO-LUTEUS.

Cyclodus nigro-luteus, (Wagl.), Gray, Cat. Liz. p. 104; Quoy & Gaim. Voy. Uran. Rept. pl. 41. (*Scincus*).
Tasmania and Houtman's Abrolhos.

85. CYCLODUS OCCIPITALIS.

Cyclodus occipitalis, Peters, MB. Berl. Acad. 1863, p. 231.
Adelaide and Swan River.

86. CYCLODUS ADELAIDENSIS.

Cyclodus adelaidensis, Peters, MB. Berl. Acad. 1863, p. 231.
Adelaide and Swan River.

87. CYCLODUS PETERSII.

Cyclodus petersii, Strauch, Bull. Acad. St. Petersb. 1866, X, p. 449.
—?

88. CYCLODUS FASCIATUS.

Cyclodus fasciatus, Lütken, Vid. Medd. 1863, p. 292, tab. 1 & 2, fig. 1.
New Holland.

89. SILUBOSAURUS STOKESII.

Silubosaurus stokesii, Gray in Stokes Trav. Austr. & Cat. Liz. p. 104.
Western Australia, (Houtman's Abrolhos).

90. SILUBOSAURUS DEPRESSUS, Günth.

This new species differs from *S. stokesii* in having the hind part of the body and especially the tail strongly depressed and flattened. The scales which in *S. stokesii* are unispinous on the tail, and partly bispinous on the back, are provided with three spines in the present species on the back of the tail as well as of the body, the central spine of each scale being the strongest. Olive-green with irregular black narrow tranverse markings or spots. Lower spots whitish, with small blackish spots.
Two specimens from Swan River are in the British Museum; the larger is five inches long.

91. EGERNIA CUNNINGHAMI.

Egernia cunninghami, Gray in Stokes Trav. Austr. & Cat. Liz. p. 105 ;=*Egernia krefftii*, Peters, MB. Berl. Acad. 1871, p. 30.
Southern and Western Australia, (Adelaide, Sydney).

92. TROPIDOLEPISMA KINGII. Plate 13.

Tropidolepisma kingii, Gray, Ann. Nat. Hist. II, p. 280, & Cat. Liz. p. 106;=*Tropidolepisma dumerilii*, Dum. Bibr. Erp. gen. V. p. 745.
Western and Southern Australia, (Houtman's Abrolhos, Swan River).

93. TROPIDOLEPISMA NITIDUM. Plate 12.

Tropidolepisma nitidum, Gray, Cat. Liz. p. 106.
Western Australia, Queensland, (Swan River, Wide Bay).

94. TROPIDOLEPISMA MAJUS. Plate 14.

Tropidolepisma majus, Gray, Cat. Liz. p. 107.
Eastern Australia, (Sydney, Rockhampton).

95. TROPIDOLEPISMA STRIOLATUM.

Tropidolepisma striolatum, Peters, MB. Berl. Acad. 1870 p. 787.
Northern Australia.

96. TROPIDOLEPISMA RICHARDI.

Tropidolepisma richardii, Peters, MB. Berl. Acad. 1869, p. 787.
Northern Australia.

97. TROPIDOLEPISMA DORSALE.

Tropidolepisma dorsale, Peters, MB. Berl. Acad. 1873, p. 642, & 1872, p. 775.
Port Bowen.

98. HETEROPUS SCHMELTZII.

Heteropus schmeltzii, Peters, MB. Berl. Acad. 1867, p. 23.
Rockhampton.

99. HETEROPUS RHOMBOIDALIS.

Heteropus rhombiodalis, Peters, MB. Berl. Acad. 1869, p. 446.
North-eastern Australia, (Port Mackay).
Scarcely distinct from *H. fuscus*; without separate central occipital shield.

100. OEDURA MARMORATA.
Plate 16, fig. 1 (juv.), and fig. 4.

Oedura marmorata, Gray, Cat. Liz. p. 147.
North-western Australia, (Port Essington).

101. OEDURA RHOMBIFERA. Plate 16, fig. 6.

Oedura rhombifera, Gray, Cat. Liz. p. 147 = *Phyllodactylus lesueurii*, Dum. Bibr. Erp. gen. III, p. 392.
Western Australia.

102. OEDURA VERRILLII.

Oedura verrillii, Cope, Proc. Acad. Philad. 1869, p. 318.
New Holland.

103. STROPHURA SPINIGERA. Plate 16, fig. 5.

Strophura spinigera, Gray, Cat. Liz. p. 148 = *Phyllodactylus strophura*, Dum. Bibr. Erp. gen. III, p. 307, pl. 32, fig. 1.
Western and Southern Australia, (Houtman's Abrolhos, Freemantle, Champion Bay, Sydney).

104. DIPLODACTYLUS VITTATUS. Plate 16, fig. 3.

Diplodactylus vittatus, Gray, Cat. Liz. p. 148.
Western and Eastern Australia, (Champion Bay, Sydney).

105. DIPDODACYTLUS ORNATUS. Plate 16, fig. 2.

Diplodactylus ornatus, Gray, Cat. Liz. p. 149 = *Diplodactylus furcosus*, Peters, MB. Berl. Acad. 1863, p. 229, & 1866, p. 446.
Western and Southern Australia, (Houtman's Abrolhos, Adelaide, New South Wales).

106. DIPLODACTYLUS OCELLATUS.
Plate 15, fig. 3, *D. bilineatus*; fig. 4. *D. ocellatus*.

Diplodactylus ocellatus, Gray, Cat. Liz. p. 149 = *Diplodactylus bilineatus*, Gray, l. c. Günth.; Ann. & Mag. Nat. Hist. 1867, XX, p. 49.
Western Australia, (Champion Bay, Houtman's Abrolhos).

107. DIPLODACTYLUS MARMORATUS. Plate 15, fig. 6.

Diplodactylus marmoratus, Gray, Cat. Liz. p. 149.
Western, and Northern Australia, (Kangaroo Island, Swan River, Freemantle, Champion Bay, Houtman's Abrolhos, Norfolk Island, Aneiteum).

108. DIPLODACTYLUS POLYOPHTHALMUS.

Diplodactylus polyophthalmus, Günth. Ann. & Mag. Nat. Hist. 1867, XX, p. 49.
Western Australia, (Champion Bay, Nicol Bay).

109. STENODACTYLOPSIS TESSELLATUS. Günth.

Back covered with comparatively large flat tessellated tubercles, which on the sides are rather smaller, scale-like and slightly imbricate. Ear opening minute. Lower parts with very small scales. Nine upper and ten lower labials. Chin shield longer than broad, whithout larger scutes behind. Tail (reproduced) with the scutes in narrow verticelli. Limbs slender, the fore-leg, if stretched forward, reaches to the nostril, the hind-leg to the axil. Whitish with faint irregular brownish spots.

Distance of snout from vent			49	mm.
„	„	„ eye	6	„
„	„	„ ear	13	„
Length of fore leg			19	„
„ hind leg			23	„

One specimen in the British Museum from Australia.

110. STENODACTYLOPSIS PULCHER.

Stenodactylopsis pulcher, Steindachner, SB. Wien. Acad. 1870, p: 343, pl. 2, figs. 3—5.
Swan River.

111. RHYNCHOEDURA ORNATA.

Rhynchoedura ornata, Günth. Ann. & Mag. Nat. Hist. 1867, XX, p. 50.
Nicol Bay.

112. PHYLLODACTYLUS ANOMALUS.

Phyllodactylus anomalus, Peters, MB. Berl. Acad., 1867, p. 14.
Queensland, (Rockhampton).
This species might be referred to *Discodactylus* (Tschudi.

113. HEMIDACTYLUS DEPRESSUS. Plate 15, fig. 1.

Hemidactylus depressus, Gray, Cat. Liz. p. 153.
Hab. ?

114. HEMIDACTYLUS BROOKII. Plate 15, fig. 2.

Hemidactylus brookii, Gray, Cat. Liz. p. 153.
Borneo and Australia.

115. HEMIDACTYLUS VITTATUS.   Plate 15, fig. 5.

Hemidactylus vittatus, Gray, Cat. Liz. p. 155.
Port Essington.

116. HEMIDACTYLUS VARIEGATUS.

Hemidactylus variegatus, Dum. Bibr. Erp. Gen. III, p. 353.
Western Australia, (Houtman's Abrolhos, Champion Bay).

117. HEMIDACTYLUS PUSILLUS.

Hemidactylus pusillus, Cope, Proc. Acad. Philad. 1869, p. 319.
South-western Australia.

118. PENTADACTYLUS BRUNNEUS.

Pentadactylus brunneus, Cope, Proc. Acad. Philad. 1869, p. 320.
New Holland.

119. GECKO TRACHYLÆMUS.

Gecko trachylæmus, Peters, M.B. Berl. Acad. 1872, p. 774.
Northern Australia

120. GEHYRA AUSTRALIS.

Gehyra australis, Gray Cat. Liz. p. 163.
Western and Northern Australia, (Swan River, Champion Bay, Port Essington, Sunday, Loyalty, and Norfolk Islands).

121. GEHYRA GRAYI.

Gehyra grayi, Steindachner in Novara, Rept. p. 11.
New South Wales.

122. NAULTINUS PACIFICUS.

Naultinus pacificus, Gray, Cat. Liz. p. 169.
New Zealand.

123. NAULTINUS GRANULATUS.

Naultinus granulatus, Gray, Cat. Liz. p. 273.
New Zealand.

124. NAULTINUS ELEGANS.

Naultinus elegans, Gray, Cat. Liz. p. 169 ; Buller, Trans. N.Z. Inst. III, p. 8, pl. 2, fig. 1.=Naultinus sulphureus, Buller, l.c.
New Zealand.

125. NAULTINUS GRAYI.

Naultinus grayi, Bell, Voy. Beagle. Rept. p. 27, pl. 14, fig. 2.
New Zealand.

126. NAULTINUS PUNCTATUS.

Naultinus punctatus, Gray, Cat. Liz. p. 169.
New Zealand.

127. NAULTINUS LINEATUS.

Naultinus lineatus, Gray, Ann. & Mag. Nat. Hist. 1869, III, p. 243.
New Zealand.

128. GONIODACTYLUS AUSTRALIS.

Goniodactylus australis, Gray, Cat. Liz. p. 172.
Hab. ?

129. HETERONOTA BINOEI.

Heteronota binoei, Gray, Cat. Liz. p. 174; Günth. Ann. & Mag. Nat. Hist. 1867, XX, p. 50 ;=*Eublepharis derbianus*, Gray, Cat. Liz. p. 274 ;=*Hoplodactylus australis*, Steindachner, Novara, Rept. p. 18, tab. 1, fig. 2.
Western and Northern Australia, (Champion Bay, Houtman's Abrolhos, Port Essington, Queensland).

130. PHYLLURUS PLATURUS.   Plate 17, fig. 3.

Phyllurus platurus, Shaw, in White, Journ. N.S. Wales, p. 246, tab. 3, fig. 2, (*Lacerta*).
Southern and Eastern Australia, (Sydney, Macquarie River).

131. PHYLLURUS MILIUSII.   Plate 17, fig. 2.

Phyllurus miliusii, (Bory St. Vincent), Gray, Cat. Liz. p. 176.
Western and Southern Australia, (Houtman's Abrolhos, Champion Bay, Adelaide, Sydney).

132. PHYLLURUS INERMIS.   Plate 17, fig. 1.

Phyllurus inermis, Gray, Cat. Liz. p. 176.
Sydney.

AGAMIDÆ.

133. GINDALIA BENNETTII.

Gindalia bennettii, Gray, Cat. Liz. p. 247.
North-western Australia.

D

134. PHYSIGNATHUS LESUEURII.

Physignathus lesueurii, Gray, Cat. Liz. p. 248;=*Istiurus lesueuri*, Dum. Bibr. Erp. gen. IV, p. 384, pl. 40, fig. 1;= *Amphibolurus heterurus*, Peters, M.B. Berl. Acad. 1866, p. 86.
Queensland, (Clarence River).

135. CHLAMYDOSAURUS KINGII.

Chlamydosaurus kingii, Gray, in King's Voy. Austr. II, pl. 1.
Queensland, Northern and North-western Australia, (Port Essington, Nicol Bay).

136. CHELOSANIA BRUNNEA.

Chelosania brunnea, Gray, Cat. Liz. p. 245.
Western Australia.

137. LOPHOGNATHUS GILBERTI. Plate 19, fig. 2.

Lophognathus gilberti, Gray, Cat. Liz. p. 250;=*Redtenbacheria fasciata*, Steindachner, Novara, Rept. p. 31.
Northern and Western Australia, (Port Essington, Champion Bay, Nicol Bay, Swan River).

138. DIPOROPHORA BILINEATA. Plate 19, fig. 1.

Diporophora bilineata, Gray, Cat. Liz. p. 250.
Northern Australia, (Port Essington, Cape York).

139. GRAMMATOPHORA CRISTATA.

Grammatophora cristata, Gray, Cat. Liz. p. 251.
Western Australia.

140. GRAMMATOPHORA MURICATA.

Grammatophora muricata, (Kaup), Gray, Cat. Liz. p. 251.
Australia generally. Rare in Tasmania.

141. GRAMMATOPHORA RETICULATA.

Grammatophora reticulata, Gray, Cat. Liz. p. 252.
Western Australia, (Nicol Bay).

142. GRAMMATOPHORA BARBATA. Plate 18, fig. 1.

Grammatophora barbata, (Kaup), Gray, Cat. Liz. p. 252.
Australia generally.

143. GRAMMATOPHORA ANGULIFERA. Plate 18, figs. 2 & 3.

Grammatophora angulifera, Gray, Cat. Liz. p. 252.
Tasmania and Western Australia.

144. GRAMMATOPHORA MACULATA.

Grammatophora maculata, Gray, Cat. Liz. p. 253;= *Grammatophora gaimardi*, Dum. & Bibr. Erp. gen. IV, p. 470.
Western and Northern Australia, (Champion Bay, Nicol Bay).

145. GRAMMATOPHORA DECRESII.

Grammatophora decresii, Dum. Bibr. Erp. gen. IV, p. 472; Peters, M.B. Berl. Acad. 1863, p. 229.
Swan River and Adelaide.

146. GRAMMATOPHORA ORNATA. Plate 18, fig. 4.

Grammatophora ornata, Gray, Cat. Liz. p. 253; Peters, M.B. Berl. Acad. 1863, p. 230.
Western and Southern Australia, (Adelaide).

147. GRAMMATOPHORA PICTA.

Grammatophora picta, Peters, M.B. Berl. Acad. 1866, p. 88, (*Amphibolurus*).
Southern Australia.

148. GRAMMATOPHORA MACROLEPIS.

Grammatophora macrolepis, Günth. Ann. & Mag. Nat. Hist. 1877, XX, p. 51.
Hab. ?

149. GRAMMATOPHORA TEMPORALIS.

Grammatophora temporalis, Günth. Ann. & Mag. Nat. Hist. 1867, XX, p. 52.
Port Essington and Nicol Bay.

150. GRAMMATOPHORA LÆVIS.

Grammatophora lœvis, Günth. Ann. & Mag. Nat. Hist. 1867, XX, p. 52.
Champion Bay.

151. GRAMMATOPHORA CALOTELLA.

Grammatophora calotella, Günth. Ann. & Mag. Nat. Hist. 1867, XX, p. 52.=*Calotella australis*, Steindachner, Novara. Rept. p. 29, tab. 1, fig. 9.
Cape York.

152. GRAMMATOPHORA CAUDICINCTA, Gütnh.

Scales small, sharply keeled, gradually increasing in size towards the median line of the back, where they are raised into a very low ridge which is developed into a low crest on the neck. An indistinct series of larger scales between the eye and ear which is large. Snout short, broad, with a distinct canthus rostralis. Nostril on the canthus rostralis directed upwards and backwards. Gular fold single. The fore and hind legs, if stretched forwards, extend somewhat beyond the nostril. Præanal and femoral pores very distinct. Upper parts nearly uniform greyish-brown. Tail with nine black rings, narrower than the interspaces between them. Lower parts whitish ; chest black ; throat slightly mottled with greyish. Total length 8 inches.

Distance between snout and vent	78	mm.
„ „ „ ear	20	„
„ „ „ eye	9	„
Length of fore leg	33	„
„ hind leg	70	„
„ fourth hind toe	14	„
„ fifth „	11	„

The specimen in the British Museum is from Nicol Bay

153. TYMPANOCRYPTIS LINEATA.

Tympanocryptis lineata, Peters, M.B, Berl. Acad.· 1863, p. 230.

Adelaide, Kangaroo Island.

154. TYMPANOCRYPTIS CEPHALUS.

Tympanocryptis cephalus, Günth. Ann. & Mag. Nat. Hist. 1867, XX, p. 52.

Nicol Bay.

155. MOLOCH HORRIDUS.

Moloch horridus, Gray, in Grey's Trav. West Austr. p. 441, pl. 2.

Southern and Western Australia, (Adelaide, Swan River).

THE LIZARDS

OF

AUSTRALIA AND NEW ZEALAND

IN THE

COLLECTION OF THE BRITISH MUSEUM.

(WITH 18 PLATES OF THE NEW SPECIES, BY MR. FORD.)

BY

JOHN EDWARD GRAY, Ph.D., F.R.S., V.P.Z.S., F.L.S., ETC

KEEPER OF THE ZOOLOGICAL COLLECTIONS IN THE BRITISH MUSEUM.

LONDON:

BERNARD QUARITCH, PICCADILLY.

MDCCCLXVII.

ALERE   FLAMMAM.

PRINTED BY TAYLOR AND FRANCIS,
RED LION COURT, FLEET STREET.

LIZARDS

OF

AUSTRALIA AND NEW ZEALAND.

Suborder LEPTOGLOSSA.

Tribe I. CYCLOSAURÆ.

Family I. MONITORIDÆ, *Gray, Cat. Lizards B. M.* 6.

1. **Odatria punctata** (T. 1.), *Gray, Cat. Lizards B. M.* 7. Monitor tristis, *Schlegel.* *Hab.* Western Australia. Var. *timorensis.* *Hab.* North Australia.

2. **Odatria ocellata** (T. 2.), *Gray, l. c.* 8; *Zool. E. & T.* t. 3. *Hab.* North-west coast of Australia.

3. **Monitor Gouldii** (T. 3), *Gray, l. c.* 12. Hydrosaurus Gouldii, *Gray, Grey's Travels,* ii. 422. *Hab.* West Australia.

4. **Hydrosaurus varius,** *Gray, l. c.* 12. Lacerta varia, *Shaw*; *White, Tour N. S. W.* t. 3. f. 2. *Hab.* New Holland.

†5. **Hydrosaurus Bellii,** *Gray, l. c.* 13. Uranus Bellii, *Dum. & Bibr. E. G.* iii. t. 35. f. 1. *Hab.* Australia.

6. **Hydrosaurus giganteus** (T. 4), *Gray, l. c.* 13; *Zool. E. & T.* t. 4. *Hab.* North coast of Australia.

Family II. LACERTINIDÆ, *Gray, l. c.* 26.

7. **Zootoca Derbiana,** *Gray, l. c.* 29. *Hab.* Australia, *Earl of Derby.*

Tribe II. GEISSOSAURÆ, *Gray, l. c.* 62.

Family II*. GYMNOPHTHALMIDÆ.

8. **Cryptoblepharus Burtonii,** *Gray, l. c.* 64. C. Peronii, *Coct. Mag. Zool.* t. . Ablepharus pœcilopleurus, *Wiegm. N. A. N. Cur.* xv. 138, t. 8. f. 1. Tiliqua Buchanani, *Gray, Ann. N. H.* ii. 291. *Hab.* Western Australia.

9. **Cryptoblepharus lineo-ocellatus,** *Gray, l. c.* 65; *Grey's Travels,* ii. 427. *Hab.* Swan River.

10. **Morethia anomala,** *Gray, l. c.* 65. *Hab.* Western Australia.

11. **Menetia Greyii,** *Gray, l. c.* 66. *Hab.* Western Australia.

12. **Miculia elegans,** *Gray, l. c.* 66. *Hab.* Western Australia.

†13. **Lerista lineata,** *Gray, l. c.* 66; *Bell, Zool. Journ.* v. 393, t. 26. f. 2. *Hab.* Australia, *Bell.*

Family III. PYGOPIDÆ, *Gray, l. c.* 67.

14. **Pypopus lepidopodus,** *Gray, l. c.* 67. Bipes lepidopodus, *Lacép. Ann. Mus.* v. t. 55. f. 1. *Hab.* Australia. Var.——. *Hab.* Swan River.

15. **Pygopus squamiceps** (T. 8. f. 3), *Gray, l. c.* 68. *Hab.* Australia.

16. **Delma Fraseri,** *Gray, l. c.* 68; *Zool. Misc.* 14; *Grey's Travels,* ii. 427, t. 4. f. 3. *Hab.* Western Australia. There is a narrow band of very small scales over the upper labial shields; the lower labial shields are large, covering the chin.

Genus NISARA.

Like *Delma,* but without any narrow band of loreal scales over the upper labial shields.

17. **Nisara Grayii.** Delma Grayii, *A. Smith, MS.* 1849, *B. M.* Olive sides, with indistinct white bands; beneath white. Tail three times as long as the body. *Hab.* Australia.

Family IV. APRASIADÆ, *Gray, l. c.* 68.

18. **Aprasia pulchella,** *Gray, l. c.* 68; *Grey's Travels Austral.* ii. 428, 438, t. 4. f. 2. *Hab.* Western Australia.

B

†19. **Aprasia octolineata,** *Peters, Monatsb. Berlin,* 1863, p. 233. *Hab.* Adelaide, Australia.

Family V. LIALISIDÆ, *Gray, l. c.* 69.

20. **Lialis Burtonii** (T. 8. f. 2), *Gray, l. c.* 69; *Grey's Travels,* ii. 437, t. 3. f. 1. *Hab.* Western Australia. Lialis bicatenata, *Gray, l. c.* 69; *Zool. Misc.* 52. *Hab.* North Australia.

21. **Lialis punctulata** (T. 8. f. 1), *Gray, l. c.* 69; *Zool. Misc.* 52. *Hab.* North Australia.

Family VI. SCINCIDÆ.

22. **Hemisphæriodon Gerrardii** (T. 9.). Hinulia Gerrardii, *Gray, l. c.* 75. H. (Hemisphæriodon) Gerrardii, *Günther.* *Hab.* Australia, Rockhampton.

23. **Hinulia elegans** (T. 10. f. 1), *Gray, l. c.* 76. *Hab.* Australia.

24. **Hinulia Greyii** (T. 10. f. 3), *Gray, l. c.* 76. *Hab.* Swan River.

25. **Hinulia tenuis** (T. 11. f. 3), *Gray, l. c.* 76. Lycosoma erucata, *Dum. & Bibr.* *Hab.* West Australia.

26. **Hinulia ornata** (T. 11. f. 1), *Gray, l. c.* 77. Tiliqua ornata, *Gray, Dieffenb. N. Z.* ii. 202. *Hab.* New Zealand.

27. **Hinulia Labillardieri,** *Gray, l. c.* 77. *Hab.* Australia, King George's Sound, Swan River.

28. **Hinulia australis,** *Gray, l. c.* 77. *Hab.* Western Australia.

29. **Hinulia Essingtonii,** *Gray, l. c.* 78. Tiliqua Essingtonii, *Gray, Zool. Misc.* 51. *Hab.* North Australia, Port Essington.

30. **Hinulia inornata** (T. 10. f. 2), *Gray, l. c.* 78. *Hab.* Western Australia, Swan River.

31. **Hinulia tæniolata,** *Gray, l. c.* 78. Lacerta tæniolata, *Shaw, White's Tour,* t. 32. f. 1. *Hab.* Australia.
Var. Lateral streaks indistinct or obliterated. *Hab.* Van Diemen's Land.

32. **Hinulia Whitii,** *Gray, l. c.* 79. Scincus Whitei, *Lacép.* Tiliqua leucopsis, *Gray, Ann. N. H.* ii. 291. *Hab.* Western Australia.

33. **Hinulia Richardsonii** (T. 11. f. 2), *Gray, l. c.* 272. *Hab.* Western Australia, Champion Bay.

34. **Hinulia fasciolata,** *Günther, Ann. & Mag. N. H.* 1867, xx. 47. *Hab.* Australia, Rockhampton.

35. **Hinulia branchialis,** *Günther, Ann. & Mag. N. H.* 1867, xx. 74. *Hab.* North-west Australia, Champion Bay.

†36. **Hinulia? striatulus.** Euprepis striatulus, *Steindachner, Reise der Novara,* p. 49. *Hab.* New South Wales (?).

37. **Mocoa Guichenoti,** *Gray, l. c.* 80. Lygosoma Guichenoti, *Dum. & Bibr.* *Hab.* Australia, King George's Sound.

38. **Mocoa trilineata,** *Gray, l. c.* 81. Tiliqua trilineata, *Gray.* Lygosoma Duperreyii, *Dum. & Bibr.* *Hab.* Western Australia.

39. **Mocoa ocellata** (T. 7. f. 3), *Gray, l. c.* 82. *Hab.* Australia.

40. **Mocoa Entrecastreauxii** (T. 7. f. 5), *Gray, l. c.* 82. *Hab.* Australia.

41. **Mocoa zelandica** (T. 7. f. 4), *Gray, l. c.* 82. Tiliqua zelandica, *Gray.* *Hab.* New Zealand.

42. **Mocoa Smithii,** *Gray, l. c.* 82. Lampropholis Smithii, *Fitz.* *Hab.* New Zealand.
See *Hinulia ornata,* var.

43. **Mocoa microtis** (T. 7. f. 2), *Gray, l. c.* 83. *Hab.* Swan River.

44. **Mocoa Owenii,** *Gray, l. c.* 272. Lacerta tæniolata, *Mus. Col. Surg.* n. 206. Ribbon-Lizard, *White, Voy.* *Hab.* Australia.

45. **Mocoa grandis,** *Gray, l. c.* 272. *Hab.* New Zealand.

46. **Carlia melanopogon** (T. 7. f. 1), *Gray, l. c.* 271. Mocoa melanopogon, *Gray, l. c.* 81. *Hab.* North Australia.

47. **Lygosoma australe,** *Gray, l. c.* 85; *Ann. & Mag. N. H.* ii. 332. *Hab.* Swan River.

48. **Lygosoma Bougainvillii,** *Gray, l. c.* 85; *Dum. & Bibr.* *Hab.* Australia.

49. **Lygosoma laterale,** *Günther, Ann. & Mag. N. H.* 1867, xx. 45. *Hab.* South Australia.

†50. **Lygosoma Schomburgkii,** *Peters, Monatsb. Berl.* 1863, p. 231. *Hab.* West Australia, Adelaide, *Schomburgk.*

51. **Tetradactylus decresiensis,** *Gray, l. c.* 86. Seps Peronii, *Fitz.* Chiamela Duvaucellii, *Gray, Ann. N. H.* ii. 333. *Hab.* Australia, Kangaroo Island, Swan River.

52. **Hemiergis decresiensis,** *Wagler; Gray, l. c.* 87. Tridactylus decresiensis, *Cuvier.* *Hab.* Kangaroo Island.

53. **Hemiergis polylepis,** *Günther, Ann. & Mag. N. H.* 1867, xx. 48. *Hab.* South Australia, *Krefft.*

54. **Chelomeles quadrilineatus,** *Gray, l. c.* 87 ; *Dum. & Bibr.* v. 774. *Hab.* West Australia, Swan River.

55. **Omolepida casuarinæ,** *Gray, l. c.* 88. Cyclodus casuarinæ, *Dum. & Bibr.* v. 749 ; *Bell, Zool. Beagle,* t. 15. f. 3. *Hab.* Van Diemen's Land.

56. **Siaphos æqualis,** *Gray, l. c.* 89. Seps æqualis, *Gray.* Hemiergis decresiensis (part.), *Dum. Hab.* Australia.

57. **Rhodona punctata,** *Gray, l. c.* 889. Ronia catenulata, *Gray, Grey's Travels,* ii. 426, t. 4. f. 1. *Hab.* West Australia.

58. **Rhodona Gerrardii,** *Günther, l. c.* 1867, xx. 46. Rhodona punctata, var. Gerrardii, *Gray. Hab.* Swan River.

59. **Rhodona punctato-vittata,** *Günther, l. c.* 47. *Hab.* Queensland.

60. **Soridia lineata,** *Gray, l. c.* 90; *Grey's Travels,* ii. 428, t. 3. f. 2. Præpedilus lineatus, *Dum. & Bibr. Hab.* West Australia.

61. **Soridia miopus,** *Günther, Ann. & Mag. N. H.* 1867, xx. 49. *Hab.* West Australia, Champion Bay.

62. **Anomalopus Verreauxii,** *Dum. & Bibr. E. G.; Günther, Ann. & Mag. N. H.* 1867, xx. 47. *Hab.* Australia, Brisbane.

63. **Plestiodon quinquelineatum,** *Gray, l. c.* 91. *Hab.* Australia ; introduced by American ship?

64. **Mabouia macrura,** *Günther, Ann. & Mag. N. H.* 1867, xx. 48. *Hab.* North Australia, Cape York.

65. **Trachydosaurus rugosus,** *Gray, l. c.* 102 ; *King's Voy. Aust.* 422, t. . Brachydactylus typicus, *A. Smith.* Trachysaurus Peronii, *Wagler. Hab.* West Australia.

66. **Trachydosaurus asper,** *Gray, l. c.* 103. *Hab.* West Australia.

67. **Cyclodus gigas,** *Gray, l. c.* 103. Scincus gigas, *Bodd.* Tiliqua Whitei, *Gray.* Lacerta scincoides, *Shaw.* C. Boddærtii, *Dum. & Bibr. Hab.* Australia, North Australia, Van Diemen's Land.

68. **Cyclodus occipitalis,** *Peters, Monatsb. Berlin,* 1863, p. 233. *Hab.* South Australia, Adelaide, *Krefft.*

69. **Cyclodus adelaidensis,** *Peters, Monatsb. Berlin,* 1863, p. 232. *Hab.* South Australia, Adelaide, *Krefft.*

70. **Cyclodus nigroluteus,** *Gray, l. c.* 104 ; *Wagler.* Scincus nigroluteum, *Quoy & Gaim. Hab.* Australia, Van Diemen's Land.

71. **Silubosaurus Stokesii,** *Gray, l. c.* 105. *Hab.* West Australia.

72. **Egernia Cunninghami,** *Gray, l. c.* 105 ; *Stokes's Travels in Aust.* t. *Hab.* Australia.

73. **Tropidolepisma Kingii** (T. 13), *Gray, l. c.* 106. Tiliqua Kingii, *Gray.* Tropidolepisma Dumerilii, *Dum. & Bibr. Hab.* Australia.

74. **Tropidolepisma nitidum** (T. 12), *Gray, l. c.* 106. *Hab.* Australia.

75. **Tropidolepisma majus** (T. 14), *Gray, l. c.* 107. T. majus, *Günther. Hab.* Australia.

Family VII. TYPHLOPSIDÆ, *Gray, l. c.* 103.

76. **Onychophis Franklinii,** *Gray, l. c.* 132. *Hab.* Australia.

77. **Anilios australis,** *Gray, l. c.* 135. *Hab.* West Australia.

78. **Anilios nigrescens,** *Gray, l. c.* 135. *Hab.* Australia, Paramatta.

† 79. **Argyrophis bramicus,** *Gray, l. c.* 138. *Hab.* Australia ?

Suborder PACHYGLOSSA.

Tribe III. NYCTISAURÆ.

Family VIII. GECKOTIDÆ, *Gray, l. c.* 142.

80. **Œdura marmorata** (T. 16. f. 4; f. 1, junior), *Gray, l. c.* 147; Phyllodactylus marmoratus, *Zool. Misc. Hab.* North Australia.

81. **Œdura rhombifera** (T. 16. f. 6), *Gray, l. c.* 147. ? Phyllodactylus Lesueurii, *Dum. & Bibr. Hab.* West Australia.

82. **Strophura spinigera** (T. 16. f. 5), *Gray, l. c.* 148. Diplodactylus spinigera, *Gray, Zool. Misc.* 53. Phyllodactylus strophiurus, *Dum. & Bibr. E. G.* iii. 301, t. 32. f. 1. *Hab.* West Australia.

83. **Diplodactylus vittatus** (T. 16. f. 3), *Gray, l. c.* 148; *P. Z. S.* 1832, p. 40. *Hab.* Australia, West Australia.

84. **Diplodactylus ornatus** (T. 16. f. 2), *Gray, l. c.* 149. *Hab.* West Australia.

85. **Diplodactylus ocellatus** (T. 15. f. 4), *Gray, l. c.* 149. *Hab.* West Australia.

86. **Diplodactylus bilineatus** (T. 15. f. 3), *Gray, l. c.* 149. *Hab.* West Australia.

87. **Diplodactylus marmoratus** (T. 15. f. 6), *Gray, l. c.* 149. *Hab.* West Australia.

88. **Diplodactylus polyophthalmus,** *Günther, Ann. & Mag. N. H.* 1867, xx. 49. *Hab.* Australia, Nicol Bay, Champion Bay.

†89. **Diplodactylus furcosus,** *Peters, Monatsb. Berlin,* 1863, p. 229. *Hab.* South Australia, Adelaide.

90. **Hemidactylus Brookii** (T. 15. f. 2), *Gray, l. c.* 153. *Hab.* Australia?

91. **Hemidactylus vittatus** (T. 15. f. 5), *Gray, l. c.* 155. *Hab.* North Australia, Borneo.

92. **Peripia variegata,** *Gray, l. c.* 159. Hemidactylus variegatus, *Dum. & Bibr. E. G.* iii. 353. *Hab.* West Australia.

†93. **Pentadactylus australis.** Hoplodactylus australis, *Steindachner, Reise der Novara,* p. 18. *Hab.* New South Wales.

94. **Gecko verus,** *Gray, l. c.* 161. *Hab.* Australia, introduced by ships?

95. **Gehyra australis,** *Gray, l. c.* 163. *Hab.* West Australia, North Australia.

†96. **Gehyra? Grayii.** Gecko Grayii, *Steindachner, Reise der Novara,* ii. *Hab.* New South Wales.

97. **Naultinus pacificus,** *Gray, l. c.* 169 and 273; *Zool. Misc.* 38. ? Platydactylus Duvaucellii, *Dum. & Bibr.* Dactylocnemis Wüllerstorfii, *Fitzinger.* Dactylocnemis pacificus, *Steindachner,* ii. Hoplodactylus Pomari, *Gerard,* 294, t. 18. f. 10–16. *Hab.* New Zealand.
Toes vary in length, perhaps a sexual variation.

98. **Naultinus granulatus,** *Gray, l. c.* 273. *Hab.* New Zealand.

99. **Naultinus elegans,** *Gray, l. c.* 169; *Zool. Misc.* 72. Gymnodactylus elegans, *Dum.* Hoplodactylus elegans, H. pacificus, H. punctatus, and H. Grayii, *Fitz.* not *Gray.* *Hab.* New Zealand.

100. **Naultinus Grayii,** *Gray, l. c.* 170; *Bell, Zool. Beagle,* 27, t. 14. f. 3.

101. **Naultinus punctatus,** *Gray, l. c.* 170; *Dieffenb. N. Z.* ii. 204; *Gerard,* 209, t. 16. f. 17–26. *Hab.* New Zealand.

102. **Goniodactylus australis,** *Gray, l. c.* 172. *Hab.* West Australia.

103. **Heteronota Binoei,** *Gray, l. c.* 174. Eublepharis derbianus, *Gray, l. c.* 274. Hoplodactylus australis, *Steindachner, Reise der Novara,* p. 18, t. 1. f. 2. *Hab.* West Australia, North Australia.

104. **Phyllurus platurus** (T. 17. f. 3), *Gray, l. c.* 176; *Cuvier.* Lacerta platurus, *Shaw.* Lacerta discosurus, *Lacép.* Stellio phyllurus, *Schneid.* *Hab.* Australia, New Holland.

105. **Phyllurus Myliusii** (T. 17. f. 2), *Gray, l. c.* 176; *Bory; Dum. & Bibr. E. G.* iii. 430, t. 33. f. 1. *Hab.* Australia, Sydney, Western Australia.

106. **Phyllurus inermis** (T. 17. f. 1), *Gray, l. c.* 176. *Hab.* Australia.

107. **Rhynchoedura ornata,** *Günther, Ann. & Mag. N. H.* 1867, xx. 51. *Hab.* Western Australia, Nicol Bay.

Tribe IV. STROBILOSAURÆ, *Gray, l. c.* 178.

Family IX. AGAMIDÆ.

108. **Chelonasia brunnea,** *Gray, l. c.* 245. *Hab.* Western Australia.

109. **Gindalia Bennettii,** *Gray, l. c.* 247. *Hab.* North-west coast of Australia.

110. **Physignathus Lesueurii,** *Gray, l. c.* 248. Lophura Lesueurii, *Gray; Dum. & Bibr. E. G.* iv. 384, t. 40. f. 1. Amphibolurus heterurus, *Peters, Monatsb.* *Hab.* Australia, Clarence River.

111. **Chlamydosaurus Kingii,** *Gray, l. c.* 249; *King, Voy. Aust.* ii. t. 1.; *Voy. au Pôle Sud,* t. 6. *Hab.* North Australia.

112. **Hatteria punctata** (T. 20.), *Gray, l. c.* 249; *Zool. Misc.* 72; Gigantic Lizard, *Cook;* Rhynchocephalus, *Owen, Trans. Geol. Soc.* vii. 80, t. 6. f. 5, 6, 7, 1845 (not described). *Hab.* New Zealand.

113. **Lophognathus Gilbertii** (T. 19. f. 2), *Gray, l. c.* 250; *Zool. Misc.* 53. Redtenbacheria fasciata, *Steindachner, Reise der Novara, Rept.* 31. *Hab.* North Australia. Swan River.

114. **Diporophora bilineata** (T. 19. f. 1), *Gray, l. c.* 250; *Zool. Misc.* 54. *Hab.* North Australia.

115. **Grammatophora cristata,** *Gray, l. c.* 251. *Hab.* Western Australia.

116. **Grammatophora muricata,** *Gray, l. c.* 251. Lacerta muricata, *Shaw.* Agama Jacksoniensis, *Kuhl.* A. grandoculus, *Lacép.* *Hab.* Western Australia, New Holland, Van Diemen's Land.

117. **Grammatophora reticulata,** *Gray, l. c.* 252. G. Decresii, *Gray,* not *Dum. & Bibr.* *Hab.* Western Australia.

118. **Grammatophora barbata** (T. 18. f. 1), *Gray, l. c.* 252. Agama barbata, *Cuvier.* *Hab.* Western Australia.

119. **Grammatophora angulifera** (T. 18. f. 3), *Gray, l. c.* 253. *Hab.* Van Diemen's Land.
Var. adelaidensis (T. 18. f. 2), *Gray, in Grey's Travels,* ii. *Hab.* Western Australia.

120. **Grammatophora maculata,** *Gray, l. c.* 253. Uromastyx maculata, *Gray.* Grammatophora Gaimardi, *Dum. &. Bibr.* iv. 470. *Hab.* Australia, Bay of Sea-dogs.

121. **Grammatophora Decresii,** *Gray, l. c.* 253; *Dum. & Bibr.* iv. 472. *Hab.* Western Australia.

122. **Grammatophora ornata** (T. 18. f. 4), *Gray, l. c.* 253. Amphibolurus ornatus, *Peters.* *Hab.* Western Australia.

123. **Grammatophora macrolepis,** *Günther, Ann. & Mag. N. H.* 1867, xx. 51. *Hab.* ——?

124. **Grammatophora lævis,** *Günther, l. c.* 52. *Hab.* Australia, Champion Bay.

125. **Grammatophora temporalis,** *Günther, l. c.* 52. *Hab.* North Australia.

126. **Grammatophora calotella,** *Günther, l. c.* 52. Calotella australis, *Steindachner, Reise der Novara,* p. 28. *Hab.* North Australia, Cape York.

†127. **Tympanocryptis lineata,** *Peters, Monatsb. Berlin,* 1863, p. 236. *Hab.* Adelaide, South Australia, *Schomburgk.*

128. **Tympanocryptis cephalus,** *Günther, Ann. & Mag. N. H.* 1867, xx. 52. *Hab.* Australia, Nicol Bay.

129. **Moloch horridus,** *Gray, l. c.* 263; *Grey's Travels in Western Australia,* t. . *Hab.* Western Australia.

THE species here quoted will be found described at length in my 'Catalogue of the Specimens of Lizards in the Collection of the British Museum,' London, 1845, 12mo, above cited, or in the Papers of Dr. Peters, Dr. Günther, or Dr. Steindachner, quoted after the species they have described. Those marked with an † are not in the British Museum Collection.

In the Plates without numbers to the figures the names are inserted under the figure; and when there are two figures, the upper name belongs to the upper, and the lower to the lower figure.

EXPLANATION OF PLATES.

EDITOR'S NOTE

In order to fit the page dimensions of this reprint, the following plates have been reduced in size from the originals: plates 3–4, 10, 12–13, and 19 (95%); 6, 14, and 17 (97%); 8 (92%); 11 (98%); 15–16 and 18 (94%); and 20 (91%). The other five plates (1–2, 5, 7, and 9) and all text pages are reprinted in the original size.

Plates 5 and 6, noted above as missing from Gray's book, "The Lizards of Australia and New Zealand" (1867), were later published by Günther in 1875, in his conclusion to the reptiles section in "The Zoology of the Voyage of H.M.S. Erebus & Terror" (see Günther's explanation on page 9). Accordingly, these two plates are inserted here in numerical order.

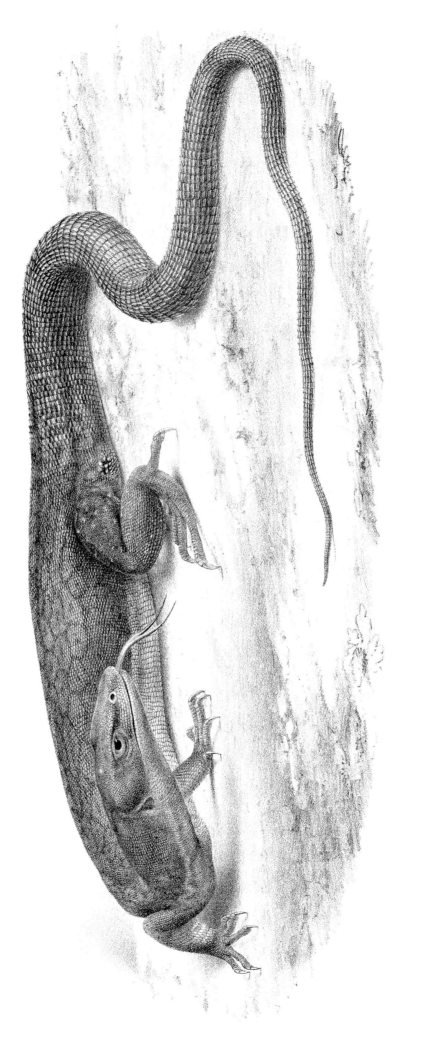

ODATRIA PUNCTATA.

MONITOR GOULDII.

HYDROSAURUS GIGANTEUS.

G.H.Ford.

Mintern Bros imp.

1. MORETHIA ANOMALA.   2. CRYPTOBLEPHARUS POECILOPLEURUS.   3. MICULIA ELEGANS.   4. MENETIA GREYI (*Enlargd.*)

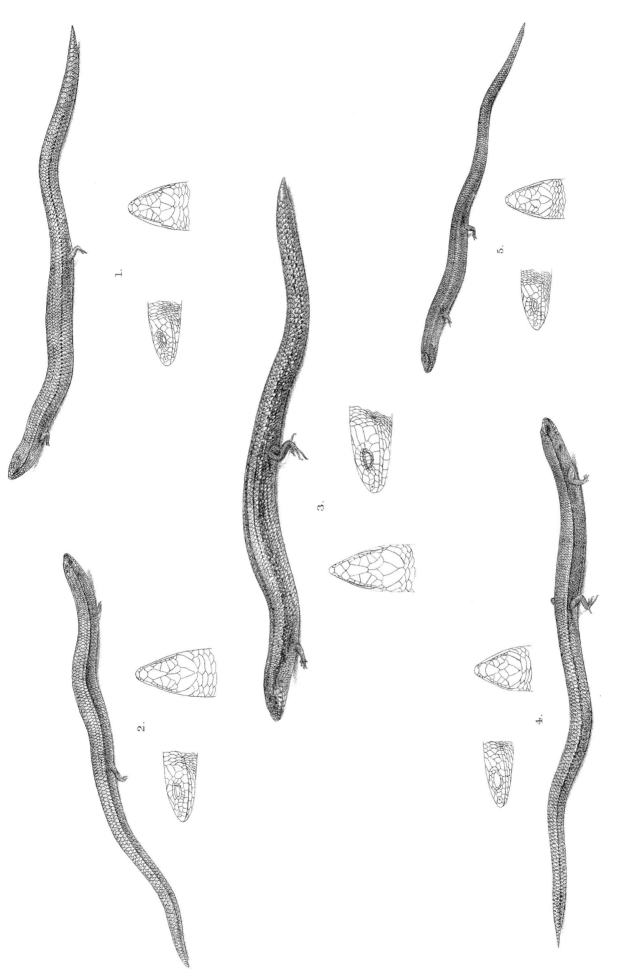

Mintern Bros. imp.

1. SIAPHOS ÆQUALIS.   2. CHELOMELES QUADRILINEATUS.   3. LYGOSOMA AUSTRALIS.
4. TETRADACTYLUS DECRESIENSIS.   5. HEMIERGIS DECRESIENSIS.

1. CARLIA MELANOPOGON.   3. MOCOA OCELLATA.

4. MOCOA ZELANDICA.

2. MOCOA MICROTIS.

5.   ,,   ENTRECASTREAUXII.

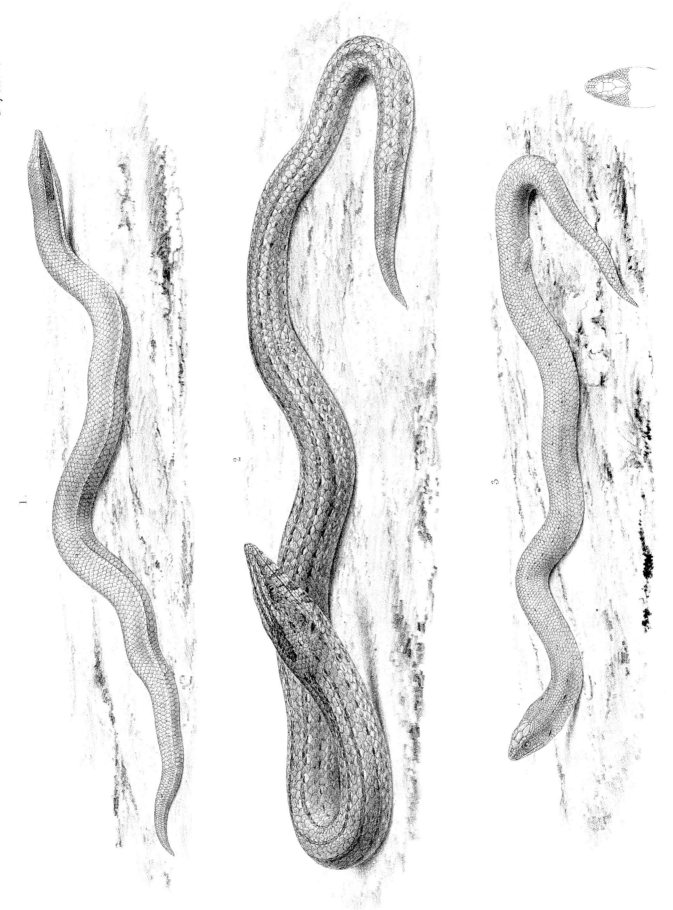

1 LIALIS PUNCTULATA 2 LIALIS BURTONIS. 3 PYGOPUS SQUAMICEPS.

Ford, del. et. lith.

Day & Haghe, lith.rs to the Queen.

HINNULIA GERRARDII.

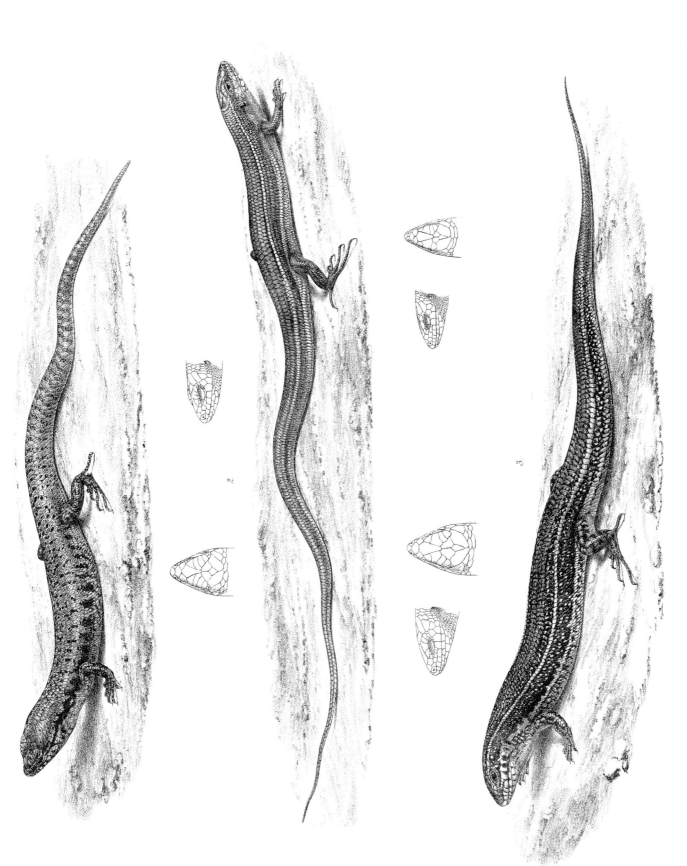

HULLMANDEL & WALTON LITH.

1. HINULIA ELEGANS.   2. HINULIA INORNATA.   3. HINULIA GREYII.

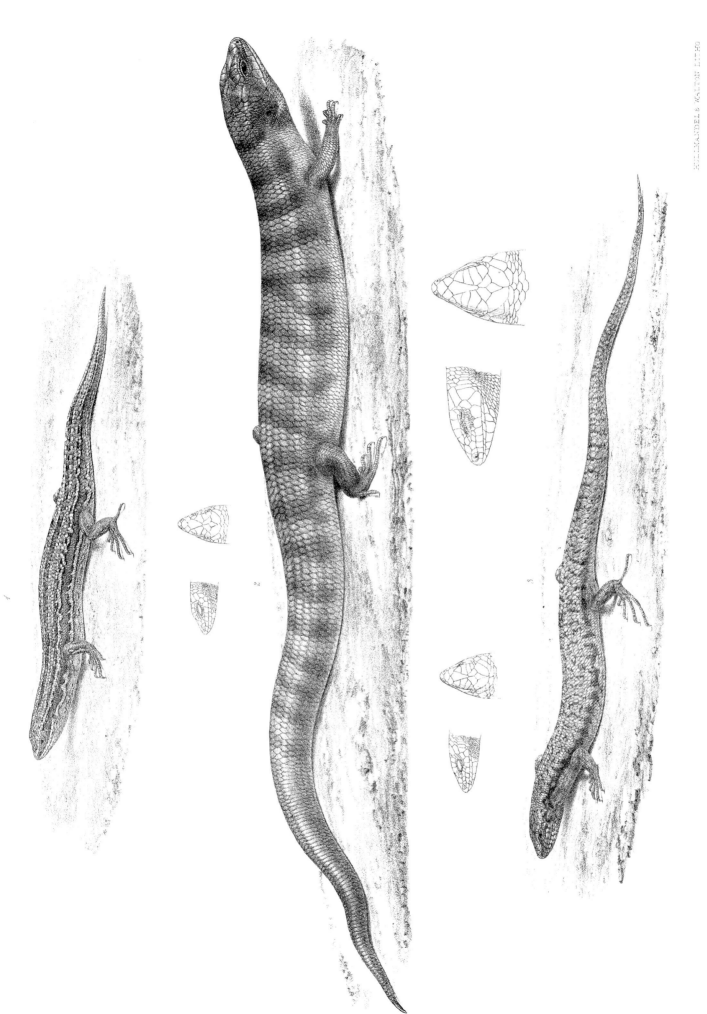

1. HINULIA ORNATA. 2. HINULIA RICHARDSONII. 3. HINULIA TENUIS.

TROPIDOLEPISMA NITIDA.

TROPIDOLEPISMA KINGII.

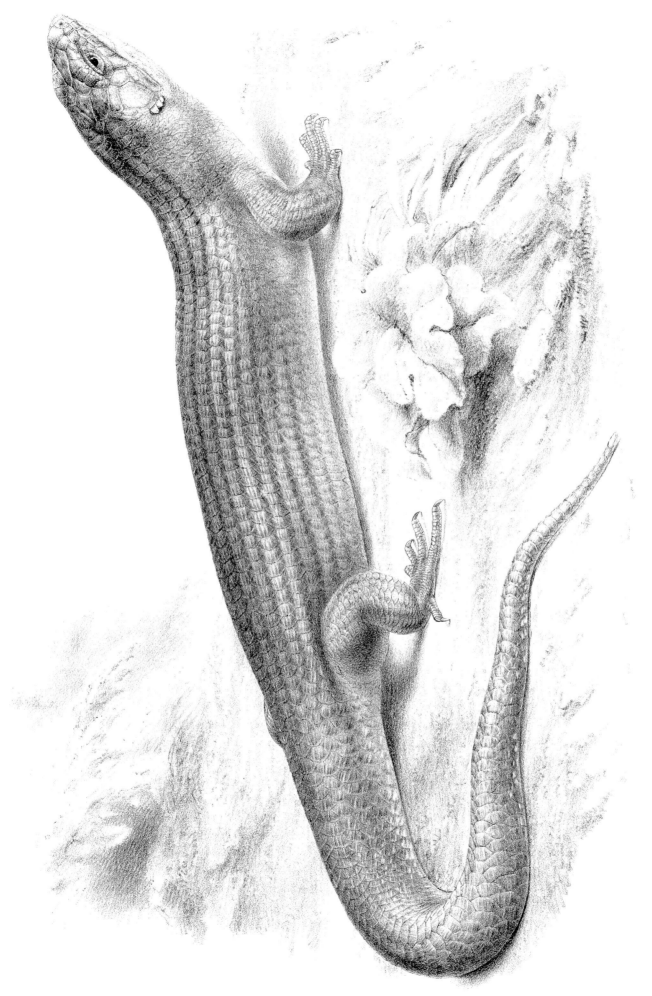

TROPIDOLEPISMA MAJOR.

H. LEMARCHE, [...] [...]

2. HEMIDACTYLUS DEPRESSUS.   1. HEMIDACTYLUS BROOKII.   3. DIPLODACTYLUS BILINEATUS, ENLARGED.

5.   ,,   VITTATUS.   4. DIPLODACTYLUS OCELLATUS.   6.   ,,   MARMORATUS.

2. DIPLODACTYLUS ORNATUS.
5. STROPHURA SPINIGERA.

1. ŒDURA MARMORATA, JUN.?
4. ,, MARMORATA.

3. DIPLODACTYLUS VITTATUS.
6. ŒDURA RHOMBIFERA.

Tab. 17.

1. PHYLLURUS INERMIS.
2.　　,,　　MYLIUSII.
3.　　,,　　PLATURUS.

Tab. 18.

1. GRAMMATOPHORA BARBATA, JUN.
2. ,, ADELAIDENSIS.
3. GRAMMATOPHORA ANGULIFERA.
4. ,, ORNATA.

TAB. 15.

1. DIPOROPHORA BILINEATA.

2. LOPHOGNATHUS GILBERTII.

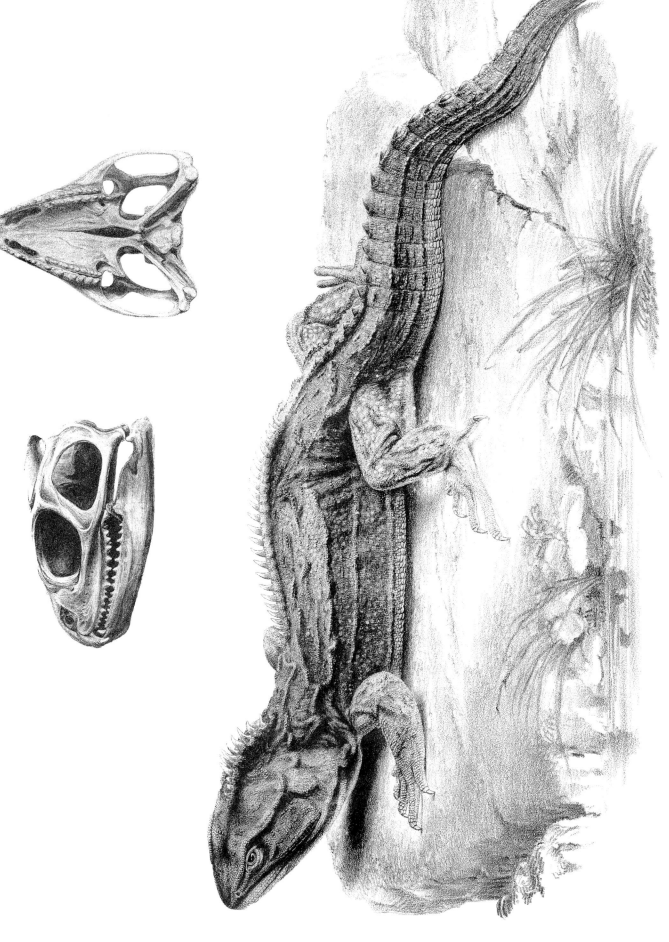

HATTERIA PUNCTATA.

PUBLICATIONS OF THE
SOCIETY FOR THE STUDY OF AMPHIBIANS AND REPTILES

SOCIETY PUBLICATIONS may be purchased from:
Dr. Robert D. Aldridge, Publications Secretary,
Department of Biology, St. Louis University,
St. Louis, Missouri 63103, USA.
(*telephone:* area code 314, 977–3910 or 977–3916;
fax: area code 314, 977–3658; *e-mail:* Aldridge@
sluvca.slu.edu).

Prices are effective through December 1996. Make checks payable to "SSAR." Shipments sent at customer's risk; however, packages can be insured at cost (see below). Overseas customers must make payment in USA funds using a draft drawn on American banks (include an additional amount to cover bank conversion charges) or by International Money Order. All persons may charge to MasterCard or VISA (provide account number and expiration date); items marked "out-of-print" are no longer available.

Shipping and Handling Costs

Shipments inside the USA: Shipping costs are in addition to the price of publications. Add an amount for shipping of the first item ($2.00 for a book costing $10.00 or more or $1.00 if the item costs less than $10.00) plus an amount for any additional items ($1.00 each for books costing over $10.00 and $0.50 for each item costing less than $10.00).

   Shipments outside the USA: Determine the cost for shipments inside USA (above) and then add 4% of the total cost of the order.

   Insurance costs: For shipments inside the USA, add $1.00 for each $50.00 value of order; outside the USA, instead add $2.00 for each $50.00 of value.

CONTRIBUTIONS TO HERPETOLOGY

Book-length monographs, comprising taxonomic revisions, results of symposia, and other major works. Prepublication discount to Society members.

No. 1. *Reproductive Biology and Diseases of Captive Reptiles,* by James B. Murphy and Joseph T. Collins (eds.). 1980. Results of a Society-sponsored symposium, including papers by 37 leading specialists. 287 p., illus. Paperbound. Out-of-print.

No. 2. *The Turtles of Venezuela,* by Peter C. H. Pritchard and Pedro Trebbau. 1984. An exhaustive natural history covering half of the turtle species of South America. 414 p., 48 color plates (25 watercolor portraits by Giorgio Voltolina and 165 photographs of turtles and habitats) measuring 8½ × 11 inches, keys, 16 maps. Regular edition, clothbound $45.00; patron's edition, two leatherbound volumes in cloth-covered box, signed and numbered by authors and artist $300.00. (*Also:* set of 25 color prints of turtle portraits on heavy paper stock, in protective wrapper $30.00.)

No. 3. *Introduction to the Herpetofauna of Costa Rica / Introducción a la Herpetofauna de Costa Rica,* by Jay M. Savage and Jaime Villa R. 1986. Bilingual edition in English and Spanish, with distribution checklist, bibliographies, and extensive illustrated keys. 220 p., one color plate, map. Clothbound $30.00.

No. 4. *Studies on Chinese Salamanders,* by Ermi Zhao, Qixiong Hu, Yaoming Jiang, and Yuhua Yang. 1988. Evolutionary review of all Chinese species with keys, diagnostic figures, and distribution maps. 80 p., 7 plates (including 10 color photographs of salamanders and habitats). Clothbound $12.00.

No. 5. *Contributions to the History of Herpetology,* by Kraig Adler, John S. Applegarth, and Ronald Altig. 1989. Biographies of 152 prominent herpetologists (with portraits and signatures), index to 2500 authors in taxonomic herpetology, and academic lineages of 1450 herpetologists. International coverage. 202 p., 148 photographs, 1 color plate. Clothbound $20.00.

No. 6. *Snakes of the* Agkistrodon *Complex: A Monographic Review,* by Howard K. Gloyd and Roger Conant. 1990. Comprehensive treatment of 33 taxa of pitvipers included in four genera: *Agkistrodon, Calloselasma, Deinagkistrodon,* and *Hypnale*. Also includes nine supplementary chapters by leading specialists. 620 p., 33 color plates (247 photographs of snakes and habitats), 20 uncolored plates, 60 text figures, checklist and keys, 6 charts, 28 maps. Clothbound $75.00. (*Also:* separate set of the 247 color photographs of snakes and habitats [on 32 plates], in protective wrapper. $30.00; limited-edition print of the book's frontispiece illustrating snakes of all four genera, from watercolor by David M. Dennis. Signed individually by Roger Conant and the artist $25.00.)

No. 7. *The Snakes of Iran*, by Mahmoud Latifi. 1991. Review of the 60 species of Iranian snakes, covering general biology, venoms, and snake bite. Appendix and supplemental bibliography by Alan E. Leviton and George R. Zug. 167 p., 22 color plates of snakes (66 figures), 2 color relief maps, 44 species range maps. Clothbound $22.00.

No. 8. *Handbook to Middle East Amphibians and Reptiles*, by Alan E. Leviton, Steven C. Anderson, Kraig Adler, and Sherman A. Minton. 1992. Annotated checklist, illustrated key, and identification manual covering 148 species and subspecies found in region from Turkish border south through the Arabian Peninsula (including Bahrain, Qatar, and United Arab Emirates) and the Arabian (Persian) Gulf. Chapters on venomous snakes and snakebite treatment plus extensive bibliography. 264 p., 32 color plates (220 photographs), maps, text figures. Clothbound $28.00.

No. 9. *Herpetology: Current Research on the Biology of Amphibians and Reptiles*. 1992. Proceedings of the First World Congress of Herpetology (1989), with a foreword by H.R.H. Prince Philip, Duke of Edinburgh. Includes the plenary lectures, a summary of the congress, and a list of delegates with their current addresses. 225 p., 28 photographs. Clothbound $28.00.

No. 10. *Herpetology of China*, by Ermi Zhao and Kraig Adler. 1993. Comprehensive review of Chinese amphibians and reptiles, including Hong Kong and Taiwan. 522 p., 48 color plates (371 photographs illustrating all 164 genera and half of the 661 species), portraits, text figures, maps. Clothbound $60.00.

No. 11. *Captive Management and Conservation of Amphibians and Reptiles*, by James B. Murphy, Kraig Adler, and Joseph T. Collins (eds.). 1994. Results of a Society-sponsored symposium, including chapters by 70 leading specialists. 408 p., 35 photographs, 1 color plate. Clothbound $58.00.

FACSIMILE REPRINTS IN HERPETOLOGY

Exact reprints of classic and important books and papers. Most titles have extensive new introductions by leading authorities. Prepublication discount to Society members.

ANDERSON, J. 1896. *Contribution to the Herpetology of Arabia.* Introduction and new checklist of Arabian amphibians and reptiles by Alan E. Leviton and Michele L. Aldrich. 160 p., illus. (one plate in color), map. Clothbound $25.00.

BELL, T. 1842–1843. *Herpetology of the "Beagle."* Part 5 of Charles Darwin's classic, "Zoology of the Voyage of H.M.S. Beagle," containing descriptions of amphibians and reptiles collected on the expedition. Introduction by Roberto Donoso-Barros. 100 p., 20 plates (measuring 8½ × 11 inches), map. Paperbound 13.00, clothbound $18.00.

BOGERT, C. M., and R. MARTÍN DEL CAMPO. 1956. *The Gila Monster and Its Allies.* The standard work on lizards of the family Helodermatidae. New preface by Charles M. Bogert and retrospective essay by Daniel D. Beck. 262 p., color plate, 62 photographs, 35 text figures, index. $38.00. (*Also:* limited edition print of the book's frontispiece illustrating a Gila monster, from watercolor by David M. Dennis. Signed individually by Charles Bogert and the artist $25.00.)

BOJANUS, L. H. 1819–1821. *Anatome Testudinis Europaeae.* The standard atlas of turtle anatomy. Introduction by Alfred Sherwood Romer. 200 p., 40 foldout plates. Out-of-print.

BOULENGER, G. A. 1877–1920. *Contributions to American Herpetology.* A collection of papers (from various journals) covering North, Central, and South American species, with an introduction by James C. Battersby. Complete in 18 parts totalling 880 p., numerous illustrations, index. Paperbound. Complete set: 18 parts plus index and two tables of contents (for binding in two volumes), in parts as issued $55.00.

BULLETIN OF THE ANTIVENIN INSTITUTE OF AMERICA. Volumes 1–5, 1927–1932. Introduction by Sherman A. Minton. 575 p., 163 photographs, maps, index. Out-of-print.

CAMP, C. L. 1923. *Classification of the Lizards.* The foundation of modern lizard systematics. New preface by the author and an introduction by Garth Underwood. 220 p., 112 figures, index. Out-of-print.

CHANG, M. L. Y. 1936. *Amphibiens Urodèles de la Chine.* The classic work on Chinese salamanders, with a new checklist by Arden H. Brame. 168 p., illus., 5 plates. Out-of-print.

COPE, E. D. 1864. *Papers on the Higher Classification of Frogs.* Reprinted from Proceedings of the Academy of Natural Sciences of Philadelphia and Natural History Review. 32 p. Paperbound $3.00.

COPE, E. D. 1871. *Catalogue of Batrachia and Reptilia Obtained by McNiel in Nicaragua; Catalogue of Reptilia and Batrachia Obtained by Maynard in Florida.* 8 p. Paperbound $1.00.

COPE, E. D. 1892. *The Osteology of the Lacertilia.* An important contribution to lizard anatomy, reprinted from Proceedings of the American Philosophical Society. 44 p., 6 plates. Paperbound $4.00.

COWLES, R. B., and C. M. BOGERT. 1944. *A Preliminary Study of the Thermal Requirements of Desert Reptiles.* The foundation of thermoregulation biology, with extensive review of recent studies by F. Harvey Pough. Reprinted from Bulletin of American Museum of Natural History. 52 p., 11 plates. Paperbound $5.00.

DUNN, E. R. 1926. *Salamanders of the Family Plethodontidae.* A recognized classic treatment of the plethodontid salamanders, including tropical and European species. Introductions by David B. Wake and Arden H. Brame. 480 p., illus., 3 plates, 86 maps, index. Out-of-print.

ESCHSCHOLTZ, F. 1829–1833. *Zoologischer Atlas* (herpetological sections). Descriptions of new reptiles and amphibians from California and the Pacific. Introduction by Kraig Adler. 32 p., 4 plates (measuring 8½ × 11 inches). Paperbound $3.00.

ESPADA, M. JIMÉNEZ DE LA. 1875. *Vertebrados del Viaje al Pacifico: Batracios.* Major taxonomic work on South American frogs. Introduction by Jay M. Savage. 208 p., 6 plates, maps. Clothbound $20.00.

FAUVEL, A.-A. 1879. *Alligators in China.* Original description of *Alligator sinensis*, including classical and natural history. 42 p., 3 plates. Paperbound $5.00.

FITZINGER, L. J. 1843. *Systema Reptilium.* An important nomenclatural landmark for herpetology, including Amphibia as well as reptiles; world-wide in scope. Introduction by Robert Mertens. 128 p., index. Paperbound $15.00.

GLOYD, H. K. 1940. *The Rattlesnakes, Genera* Sistrurus *and* Crotalus. Introduction and new checklist by Hobart M. Smith and Herbert M. Harris. 300 p., plus 31 plates of photographs, index. Out-of-print.

GRAY, J. E. 1825. *A Synopsis of the Genera of Reptiles and Amphibia.* Reprinted from Annals of Philosophy. 32 p. Paperbound $3.00.

GRAY, J. E. 1831–1844. *Zoological Miscellany.* A privately printed journal, devoted mostly to descriptions of amphibians, reptiles, and birds from throughout the world. Introduction by Arnold G. Kluge. 86 p., 4 plates. Paperbound $6.00, clothbound $10.00.

GRAY, J. E., and A. GÜNTHER. 1845–1875. *Lizards of Australia and New Zealand.* The reptile section from "Voyage of H.M.S Erebus and Terror," together with Gray's 1867 book on the same subject. Introduction by Glenn M. Shea. 80 p., 20 plates (measuring 8½ × 11 inches). Clothbound $20.00.

GÜNTHER, A. 1885–1902. *Biologia Centrali-Americana. Reptilia and Batrachia.* The standard work on Middle American herpetology with 76 full-page plates measuring 8½ × 11 inches (12 in color). Introductions by Hobart M. Smith, A. E. Gunther, and Kraig Adler. 575 p., photographs, maps. Clothbound $50.00. (*Also:* separate set of the 12 color plates, in protective wrapper $18.00.)

HOLBROOK, J. E. 1842. *North American Herpetology.* Five volumes bound in one. The classic work by the father of North American herpetology. Exact facsimile of the definitive second edition, including all 147 plates, measuring 8½ × 11 inches (20 reproduced in full color). Introduction and checklists by Richard and Patricia Worthington and by Kraig Adler. 1032 p. Leatherbound patron's edition, out-of-print; regular edition, clothbound $60.00.

JUNIOR SOCIETY OF NATURAL SCIENCES (CINCINNATI, OHIO). 1930–1932. Herpetological papers from the society's Proceedings, with articles by Weller, Walker, Dury, and others. 56 p. Paperbound $3.00.

KIRTLAND, J. P. 1838. *Zoology of Ohio* (herpetological portion). 8 p. Paperbound $1.00.

LeCONTE, J. E. 1824–1828. *Three Papers on Amphibians,* from the Annals of the Lyceum of Natural History, New York. 16 p. Paperbound $2.00.

LINNAEUS, C. 1766–1771. *Systema Naturae* (ed. 12) and *Mantissa Plantarum* (herpetological portions from both). 56 p. Introduction by Kraig Adler. Out-of-print.

LOVERIDGE, A. 1946. *Reptiles [and Amphibians] of the Pacific.* The standard review of the herpetofauna of the Pacific region including Australia and extending from Indonesia to Hawaii and the Galápagos Islands. 271 p., 7 plates, 1 double-page map, index. Out-of-print.

McILHENNY, E. A. 1935. *The Alligator's Life History*. The most complete natural history of the American alligator. Introduction by Archie Carr and a review of recent literature by Jeffrey W. Lang. 125 p., 18 photographs and a portrait. Clothbound $20.00.

McLAIN, R. B. 1899. *Contributions to North American Herpetology*. Three privately printed papers containing important distributional records and the description of a new form. 28 p., index. Paperbound $2.00.

ORBIGNY, A. D' [and G. BIBRON]. 1847. *Voyage dans l'Amérique Méridionale*. This extract comprises the complete section on reptiles and amphibians from this voyage to South America. 14 p., 9 plates measuring 8½ × 11 inches. $3.00.

PETERS, W. 1838–1883. *The Herpetological Contributions of Wilhelm C. H. Peters (1815–1883)*. A collection of 174 titles, world-wide in scope, and including Peters' book, "Reise nach Mossambique." Biography and annotated bibliography by Aaron M. Bauer, Rainer Günther, and Meghan Klipfel. About 700 pages, 114 plates, 9 photographs, maps, index. Clothbound, in press.

RAFINESQUE, C. S. 1820. *Annals of Nature* (herpetological and ichthyological sections), 4 p. Paperbound $1.00.

RAFINESQUE, C. S. 1822. *On Two New Salamanders of Kentucky*. 2 p. Paperbound $1.00.

RAFINESQUE, C. S. 1832–1833. *Five Herpetological Papers from the Atlantic Journal*. 4 p. Paperbound $1.00.

SOWERBY, J. DeC., E. LEAR, and J. E. GRAY. 1872. *Tortoises, Terrapins, and Turtles Drawn From Life*. The finest atlas of turtle illustrations ever produced. Introduction by Ernest E. Williams. 26 p., 61 full-page plates (measuring 8½ × 11 inches). Clothbound $25.00.

SPIX, J. B. VON, and J. G. WAGLER. 1824–1825. *Herpetology of Brazil*. The most comprehensive and important early survey of Brazilian herpetology. Introduction by P. E. Vanzolini. 400 p., 98 plates, one in color (each measuring 8½ × 11 inches), map. Clothbound $36.00.

TROSCHEL, F. H. 1850 [1852]. Cophosaurus texanus, *neue Eidechsengattung aus Texas*. 8 p. Paperbound $1.00.

TSCHUDI, J. J. VON. 1838. *Classification der Batrachier*. A major work in systematic herpetology, with introduction by Robert Mertens. 118 p., 6 plates. Paperbound $18.00.

TSCHUDI, J. J. VON. 1845. *Reptilium Conspectus*. Descriptions of new reptiles and amphibians from Peru. 24 p. Paperbound $2.00.

VANDENBURGH, J. 1895–1896. *Herpetology of Lower California*. Herpetology of Baja California, Mexico (collected papers). 101 p., 11 plates, index. Paperbound $8.00.

WAITE, E. R. 1929. *The Reptiles and Amphibians of South Australia*. Introduction by Michael J. Tyler and Mark Hutchinson. 282 p., color plate, portrait, 192 text figures including numerous photographs. Clothbound $35.00.

WIEGMANN, A. F. A. 1834. *Herpetologia Mexicana*. Introduction by Edward H. Taylor. 66 p., 10 plates (folio, measuring 10 × 14 inches). Out-of-print.

WILCOX, E. V. 1891. *Notes on Ohio Batrachians*. 3 p. Paperbound $1.00.

WILLISTON, S. W. 1925. *Osteology of the Reptiles*. Covers living and extinct forms, with introduction by Claude W. Hibbard. 304 p., 191 text figures, index. Out-of-print.

WRIGHT, A. H., and A. A. WRIGHT. 1962. *Handbook of Snakes of the United States and Canada, Volume 3, Bibliography*. Out-of-print since about 1969, this cross-indexed bibliography is a necessary companion to Volumes 1 and 2. 187 p. Clothbound $18.00.

HERPETOLOGICAL REVIEW
AND H.I.S.S. PUBLICATIONS

The Society's official newsletter, international in coverage. In addition to news notes and feature articles, regular departments include regional societies, techniques, husbandry, life history, geographic distribution, and book reviews. Issued quarterly as part of Society membership or separately by subscription. All numbers are paperbound as issued and measure 8½ × 11 inches. In 1973, publications of the Herpetological Information Search Systems (*News-Journal* and *Titles and Reviews*) were substituted for *Herpetological Review*; content and format are the same.

Volume 1 (1967–1969), numbers 1–9, $4.00 per number.
Volumes 2–25 (1970–1994), four numbers in each volume (except volumes 3–4, with 6 numbers each), $4.00 per number.
The following numbers are out-of-print and *no longer available*: Volume 1 (number 7), 3(2, 6), 4(1), 5(1, 2), 6(1, 2, 4), 7(3, 4), and 10(2).
Cumulative Index for Volumes 1–7 (1967–1976), 60 pages, $4.00.
Cumulative Index for Volumes 1–17 (1967–1986), 90 pages, $7.00.
H.I.S.S. Publications: News-Journal, volume 1, numbers 1–6, and Titles and Reviews, volume 1, numbers 1–2 (all of 1973–1974), complete set, $10.00.
Index to Geographic Distribution Records for Volumes 1–17 (1967–1986), including H.I.S.S. publications, 44 pages, $5.00.

CATALOGUE OF
AMERICAN AMPHIBIANS AND REPTILES

Loose-leaf accounts of taxa (measuring 8½ × 11 inches) prepared by specialists, including synonymy, definition, description, distribution map, and comprehensive list of literature for each taxon. Covers amphibians and reptiles of the entire Western Hemisphere. Issued by subscription. Individual accounts are not sold separately.

CATALOGUE ACCOUNTS:
    Complete set: Numbers 1–600, $300.00.
    Partial sets: Numbers 1–190, $60.00.
                    Numbers 191–410, $70.00.
                    Numbers 411–600, $150.00.
INDEXES TO ACCOUNTS 1–400: Cross-referenced, 64 pages, $5.00; accounts 401–600: Cross-referenced, 32 pages, $5.00.
IMPRINTED POST BINDER: $35.00. (Note: one binder holds about 200 accounts.)
SYSTEMATIC TABS: Ten printed tabs for binder, such as "Class Amphibia," "Order Caudata," etc., $5.00 per set.

JOURNAL OF HERPETOLOGY

The Society's official scientific journal, international in scope. Issued quarterly as part of Society membership. All numbers are paperbound as issued, measuring 7 × 10 inches.

Volume 1 (1968), numbers 1–4 combined.
Volumes 2–5 (1968–1971), numbers 1–2 and 3–4 combined, $6.00 per double number.
Volume 6 (1972), numbers 1, 2, and double number 3–4.
Volumes 7–28 (1973–1994), four numbers in each volume, $6.00 per single number.
The following volumes and numbers are out-of-print and are *no longer available*: Volume 1, 2, 3, 4, 5(3, 4), 6, 7(1), 8(1), 9(1, 2, 4), 10(1, 4), 11(4), and 12(1, 2).
Cumulative Index for Volumes 1–10 (1968–1976), 72 pages, $7.00.

HERPETOLOGICAL CIRCULARS

Miscellaneous publications of general interest to the herpetological community. All numbers are paperbound, as issued. Prepublication discount to Society members.

No. 1. *A Guide to Preservation Techniques for Amphibians and Reptiles* by George R. Pisani. 1973. 22 p., illus. $3.00.

No. 2. *Guía de Técnicas de Preservación de Anfibios y Reptiles* por George R. Pisani y Jaime Villa. 1974. 28 p., illus. $3.00.

No. 3. *Collections of Preserved Amphibians and Reptiles in the United States* compiled by David B. Wake (chair) and the Committee on Resources in Herpetology. 1975. 22 p. Out-of-print.

No. 4. *A Brief Outline of Suggested Treatments for Diseases of Captive Reptiles* by James B. Murphy. 1975. 13 p. $3.00.

No. 5. *Endangered and Threatened Amphibians and Reptiles in the United States* compiled by Ray E. Ashton, Jr. (chair) and 1973–74 SSAR Regional Herpetological Societies Liaison Committee. 1976. 65 p. Out-of-print.

No. 6. *Longevity of Reptiles and Amphibians in North American Collections* by J. Kevin Bowler. 1977. 32 p. $3.00. (See also number 21.)

No. 7. *Standard Common and Current Scientific Names for North American Amphibians and Reptiles* (1st ed.) by Joseph T. Collins, James E. Huheey, James L. Knight, and Hobart M. Smith. 1978. 36 p. $3.00. (See also numbers 12 and 19.)

No. 8. *A Brief History of Herpetology in North America Before 1900* by Kraig Adler. 1979. 40 p., 24 photographs, 1 map. $3.00.

No. 9. *A Review of Marking Techniques for Amphibians and Reptiles* by John W. Ferner. 1979. 42 p., illus. $3.00.

No. 10. *Vernacular Names of South American Turtles* by Russell A. Mittermeier, Federico Medem and Anders G. J. Rhodin. 1980. 44 p. $3.00.

No. 11. *Recent Instances of Albinism in North American Amphibians and Reptiles* by Stanley Dyrkacz. 1981. 36 p. $3.00.

No. 12. *Standard Common and Current Scientific Names for North American Amphibians and Reptiles* (2nd ed.) by Joseph T. Collins, Roger Conant, James E. Huheey, James L. Knight, Eric M. Rundquist, and Hobart M. Smith. 1982. 32 p. $3.00. (See also numbers 7 and 19.)

No. 13. *Silver Anniversary Membership Directory*, including addresses of all SSAR members, addresses and publications of the herpetological societies of the world, and a brief history of the Society. 1983. 56 p., 4 photographs. $3.00.

No. 14. *Checklist of the Turtles of the World with English Common Names* by John Iverson. 1985. 14 p. $3.00.

No. 15. *Cannibalism in Reptiles: A World-Wide Review* by Joseph C. Mitchell. 1986. 37 p. $4.00.

No. 16. *Herpetological Collecting and Collections Management* by John E. Simmons. 1987. 72 p., 6 photographs. $6.00.

No. 17. *An Annotated List and Guide to the Amphibians and Reptiles of Monteverde, Costa Rica* by Marc P. Hayes, J. Alan Pounds, and Walter W. Timmerman. 1989. 70 p., 32 figures. $5.00.

No. 18. *Type Catalogues of Herpetological Collections: An Annotated List of Lists* by Charles R. Crumly. 1990. 50 p. $5.00.

No. 19. *Standard Common and Current Scientific Names for North American Amphibians and Reptiles* (3rd ed.) compiled by Joseph T. Collins (coordinator for SSAR Common and Scientific Names List). 1990. 45 p. $5.00. (See also numbers 7 and 12.)

No. 20. *Age Determination in Turtles* by George R. Zug. 1991. 32 p., 6 figures. $5.00.

No. 21. *Longevity of Reptiles and Amphibians in North American Collections* (2nd ed.) by Andrew T. Snider and J. Kevin Bowler. 1992. 44 p. $5.00. (See also number 6.)

No. 22. *Biology, Status, and Management of the Timber Rattlesnake* (Crotalus horridus): *A Guide for Conservation* by William S. Brown. 1993. 84 p., 16 color photographs. $8.00.

No. 23. *Scientific and Common Names for the Amphibians and Reptiles of Mexico in English and Spanish / Nombres Científicos y Comunes en Ingles y Español de los Anfibios y los Reptiles de México* by Ernest A. Liner. Spanish translation by José L. Camarillo R. 1994. 118 p. $12.00.

PUBLICATIONS OF
THE OHIO HERPETOLOGICAL SOCIETY

OHS was the predecessor to the Society for the Study of Amphibians and Reptiles. All publications international in scope. Paperbound as issued.

Volume 1 numbers 1–4, plus Special Publications 1–2 (all 1958), facsimile reprint, out-of-print.

Volume 2 (1959–1960), four numbers, $2.00 per number; numbers 3 and 4 out-of-print.

Volume 3 (1961–1962), four numbers, $1.00 per number; numbers 1 and 3 out-of-print.

Volume 4 (1963–1964), four numbers; double number 1–2, $4.00, numbers 3 and 4 $2.00 each.

Volume 5 (1965–1966), four numbers, $2.00 per number.

Special Publications 3–4 (1961–1962), $2.00 per number; number 3 out-of-print.

PRODUCTION SPECIFICATIONS

WORD PROCESSING AND FORMATTING OF INTRODUCTION: Cornell University, Ithaca, New York, USA (Timothy D. Perry). Type set in New Century Schoolbook, using the Aldus PageMaker 4.2 program on a Macintosh IIci computer, and was printed on an Apple LaserWriter IIg printer.

PRINTING AND BINDING: Thomson-Shore, Inc., Dexter, Michigan, USA (Ned Thomson, Lana Paton, Merry Sumner). The book is printed on 80-pound Mead Moistrite Matte text stock, a recycled paper. It is covered in Roxite C cloth (linen finish) with Multicolor Antique end papers.

PAPER: All paper in this book is acid- and groundwood-free. It meets the guidelines for permanence and durability of the Committee on Publication Guidelines for Book Longevity of the Council on Library Resources.

DATE OF PUBLICATION: 1 June 1995.

PLACE OF PUBLICATION: Ithaca, New York, USA.

NUMBER OF COPIES: 1,000 books.
500 sets of plates.

•